Student Solution

An Introduction to
Mathematical
Statistics
and Its Applications

Third Edition

Richard J. Larsen · Morris L. Marx

Prentice
Hall

Upper Saddle River, NJ 07458

Acquisitions Editor: Kathy Boothby Sestak
Supplement Editor: Joanne Wendelken
Special Projects Manager: Barbara A. Murray
Production Editor: Dawn Murrin
Supplement Cover Manager: Paul Gourhan
Supplement Cover Designer: PM Workshop Inc.
Manufacturing Buyer: Lisa McDowell

© 2001 by Prentice Hall
Upper Saddle River, NJ 07458

Printed in the United States of America

10 9 8 7 6 5 4 3 2 1

ISBN 0-13-031015-8

Prentice-Hall International (UK) Limited, London
Prentice-Hall of Australia Pty. Limited, Sydney
Prentice-Hall Canada, Inc., Toronto
Prentice-Hall Hispanoamericana, S.A., Mexico
Prentice-Hall of India Private Limited, New Delhi
Pearson Education Asia Pte. Ltd., Singapore
Prentice-Hall of Japan, Inc., Tokyo
Editora Prentice-Hall do Brazil, Ltda., Rio de Janeiro

Table of Contents

Chapter 2

Section 2.2

2.2.1 $S = \{(s,s,s), (s,s,f), (s,f,s), (f,s,s), (s,f,f), (f,s,f), (f,f,s), (f,f,f)\}$
$A = \{(s,f,s), (f,s,s)\}; \quad B = \{(f,f,f)\}$

2.2.3 $(1,3,4), (1,3,5), (1,3,6), (2,3,4), (2,3,5), (2,3,6)$

2.2.5 Let p_1 and p_2 denote the two perpetrators and i_1, i_2, and i_3, the three in the lineup who are innocent. Then
$S = \{(p_1,i_1), (p_1,i_2), (p_1,i_3), (p_2,i_1), (p_2,i_2), (p_2,i_3), (p_1,p_2), (i_1,i_2), (i_1,i_3), (i_2,i_3)\}$
The event A contains every outcome in S except (p_1,p_2).

2.2.7 In order for the shooter to win with a point of 9, one of the following (countably infinite) sequences of sums must be rolled: (9,9), (9, no 7 or no 9,9), (9, no 7 or no 9, no 7 or no 9,9), …

2.2.9

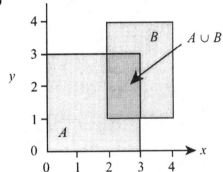

2.2.11 $A \cap B \cap C = \{x: \ x = 2, 3, 4\}$

2.2.13 a) A_1 b) A_k

2.2.15 40

2.2.17 a)

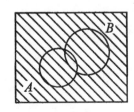

$(A \cap B)^C \;=\; A^C \cup B^C$

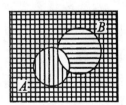

b)

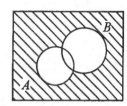 $(A \cup B)^C = A^C \cap B^C$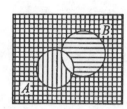

2.2.19 a) Let s be a member of $A \cup (B \cup C)$. Then s belongs to either A or $B \cup C$ (or both). If s belongs to A, it necessarily belongs to $(A \cup B) \cup C$. If s belongs to $B \cup C$, it belongs to B or C or both, so it must belong to $(A \cup B) \cup C$. Now, suppose s belongs to $(A \cup B) \cup C$. Then it belongs to either $A \cup B$ or C or both. If it belongs to C, it must belong to $A \cup (B \cup C)$. If it belongs to $A \cup B$, it must belong to either A or B or both, so it must belong to $A \cup (B \cup C)$.

b)

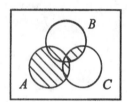 $A \cap (B \cap C) = (A \cap B) \cap C$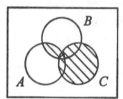

Section 2.3

2.3.1 Let L and V denote the sets of programs with offensive language and too much violence, respectively. Then $P(L) = 0.42$, $P(V) = 0.27$, and $P(L \cap V) = 0.10$. Therefore, P(program complies) $= P((L \cup V)^C) = 1 - [P(L) + P(V) - P(L \cap V)] = 0.41$.

2.3.3 a) $1 - P(A \cap B)$ [draw the Venn diagram]
b) $P(B) - P(A \cap B)$ [draw the Venn diagram]

2.3.5 No. $P(A_1 \cup A_2 \cup A_3) = P$(at least one "6" appears) $= 1 - P$(no 6's appear) $= 1 - \left(\frac{5}{6}\right)^3 \neq \frac{1}{2}$.
The A_i's are not mutually exclusive, so $P(A_1 \cup A_2 \cup A_3) \neq P(A_1) + P(A_2) + P(A_3)$.

2.3.7

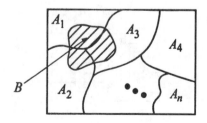

By inspection, $B = (B \cap A_1) \cup (B \cap A_2) \cup \ldots \cup (B \cap A_n)$.

2.3.9 $P(\text{odd man out}) = 1 - P(\text{no odd man out}) = 1 - P(HHH \text{ or } TTT) = 1 - \dfrac{2}{8} = \dfrac{3}{4}.$

2.3.11   Let A: State wins Saturday and B: State wins next Saturday. Then $P(A) = 0.10$, $P(B) = 0.30$, and $P(\text{lose both}) = 0.65 = 1 - P(A \cup B)$, which implies that $P(A \cup B) = 0.35$. Therefore, $P(A \cap B) = 0.10 + 0.30 - 0.35 = 0.05$, so $P(\text{State wins exactly once}) = P(A \cup B) - P(A \cap B) = 0.35 - 0.05 = 0.30.$

2.3.13   Let F: female is hired and T: minority is hired. Then $P(F) = 0.60$, $P(T) = 0.30$, and $P(F^C \cap T^C) = 0.25 = 1 - P(F \cup T)$. Since $P(F \cup T) = 0.75$, $P(F \cap T) = 0.60 + 0.30 - 0.75 = 0.15.$

Section 2.4

2.4.1 $P(\text{sum} = 7) = 2P(1) \cdot P(6) + 2P(2) \cdot P(5) + 2P(3) \cdot P(4) = 2\left(\dfrac{1}{4}\right)\left(\dfrac{1}{4}\right) + 2\left(\dfrac{1}{8}\right)\left(\dfrac{1}{8}\right) + 2\left(\dfrac{1}{8}\right)\left(\dfrac{1}{8}\right)$
$= 0.1875$. When the two dice are fair, $P(\text{sum} = 7) = 6/36 = 0.1667$. Cheaters would slip the shooter a pair of ace-six flats after the shooter's first roll had established the "point" that needed to be made. Doing so increases the chances that the shooter will lose by rolling a 7 before rolling the point.

2.4.3   3/10

2.4.5   Ten (unordered and equally-likely) samples of size 3 can be drawn: (1,2,3), (1,2,4), (1,2,5), (1,3,4), (1,3,5), (1,4,5), (2,3,4), (2,3,5), (2,4,5), and (3,4,5). Since "4" is the largest number appearing in three of the samples, $P(\text{largest chip is 4}) = 3/10$.

2.4.7   A total of $6^3 = 216$ outcomes are possible (and equally-likely); 12 share the property that the blue die is the sum of the other two (and all faces are different): (1,2,3), (2,1,3), (1,3,4), (3,1,4), (1,4,5), (4,1,5), (1,5,6), (5,1,6), (2,3,5), (3,2,5), (2,4,6), and (4,2,6). The desired probability, then, is 12/216.

2.4.9 $P(\text{number chosen is even}) = P(s = 2, 4, 6, \ldots) = \displaystyle\sum_{k=1}^{\infty} \dfrac{2}{3^{2k}} = 2\sum_{k=1}^{\infty}\left(\dfrac{1}{9}\right)^k = 2\left\{\sum_{k=0}^{\infty}\left(\dfrac{1}{9}\right)^k - \left(\dfrac{1}{9}\right)^0\right\} =$
$2\left\{\dfrac{1}{1 - 1/9} - 1\right\} = \dfrac{1}{4}.$

Section 2.5

2.5.1   The area under $f(y)$ equals $2(k) + 5(2k) + 1(k) = 13k$, but it must equal 1, so $k = 1/13$.

2.5.3 If $f(y) = k(y + y^2)$, $0 \le y \le 2$, then $\int_0^2 k(y + y^2)dy = \dfrac{14k}{3} = 1$, so $k = \dfrac{3}{14}$. P(pin is unusable) =

$P(y > 1) = \int_1^2 \dfrac{3}{14}(y + y^2)dy = \dfrac{23}{28}$.

2.5.5 P(batch is accepted) $= P(y < 2) = (1 - e^{-9})^{-1} \int_0^2 2ye^{-y^2} dy$. Let $u = y^2$. Then $P(y < 2) =$

$(1 - e^{-9})^{-1} \int_0^4 e^{-u}du = (1 - e^{-4}) \cdot (1 - e^{-9})^{-1}$.

2.5.7 Pictured is $f(y) = 6y(1 - y)$, $0 \le y \le 1$, superimposed over each of the two density-scaled histograms. (Note: For each class, density $= \dfrac{\text{frequency}}{(0.2)(25)} = \dfrac{\text{frequency}}{5}$). Judging from the similarity between the shapes of the histograms and the shape of $f(y)$, Data set (a) is more likely to have come from $f(y) = 6y(1 - y)$, $0 \le y \le 1$.

Data set (a)

Data set (b)

2.5.9 If $f(y) = ky^3$, $1 \le y \le 2$, $\int_1^2 ky^3 dy = \dfrac{15k}{4} = 1$, so $k = \dfrac{4}{15}$. Then y_{30} satisfies the equation

$\int_0^{y_{30}} \dfrac{4}{15} y^3 dy = 0.30$. That is, $y_{30}^4/15 = 0.30$, so $y_{30} = \sqrt[4]{4.5} = 1.46$.

2.5.11 $P(y > 1.5) = 1 - P(y \le 1.5) = 1 - \int_0^{1.5} ye^{-y}dy$. Integrating by parts gives $P(y > 1.5) =$
$1 - (1 - 2.5e^{-1.5}) = 0.56$.

Section 2.6

2.6.1 P(sum $= 10 \,|\,$ sum exceeds 8) $= \dfrac{P(\text{sum} = 10 \text{ and sum exceeds } 8)}{P(\text{sum exceeds } 8)} =$

$\dfrac{P(\text{sum} = 10)}{P(\text{sum} = 9, 10, 11, \text{ or } 12)} = \dfrac{3/36}{4/36 + 3/36 + 2/36 + 1/36} = \dfrac{3}{10}$.

2.6.3 $P(A|B) + P(B|A) = 0.75 = \dfrac{P(A\cap B)}{P(B)} + \dfrac{P(A\cap B)}{P(A)} = \dfrac{10P(A\cap B)}{4} + 5P(A\cap B)$, which

implies that $P(A\cap B) = 0.1$.

2.6.5 $P(\text{both are boys} \mid \text{at least one is a boy}) = \dfrac{P(\text{both are boys})}{P(\text{at least one is a boy})} = \dfrac{1/4}{3/4} = \dfrac{1}{3}$.

2.6.7 $P(E|A\cup B) = \dfrac{P(E\cap(A\cup B))}{P(A\cup B)} = \dfrac{P(E)}{P(A\cup B)} = \dfrac{P(A\cup B) - P(A\cap B)}{P(A\cup B)} = \dfrac{0.4 - 0.1}{0.4} = \dfrac{3}{4}$.

2.6.9 $P(A\cup B) = 0.8$ and $P(A\cup B) - P(A\cap B) = 0.6$, so $P(A\cap B) = 0.2$. Also, $P(A|B) = 0.6 = $
$\dfrac{P(A\cap B)}{P(B)}$, so $P(B) = \dfrac{0.2}{0.6} = \dfrac{1}{3}$ and $P(A) = 0.8 + 0.2 - \dfrac{1}{3} = \dfrac{2}{3}$.

2.6.11 $P(A|B) = \dfrac{P(A\cap B)}{P(B)} = \dfrac{P(A) + P(B) - P(A\cup B)}{P(B)} = \dfrac{a + b - P(A\cup B)}{b}$.

But $P(A\cup B) \le 1$, so $P(A|B) \ge \dfrac{a + b - 1}{b}$.

2.6.13 $P(y \ge r + t \mid y \ge t) = P(y \ge r + t)/P(y \ge t) = \displaystyle\int_{r+t}^{\infty} \lambda e^{-\lambda y}\,dy \Big/ \int_{t}^{\infty} \lambda e^{-\lambda y}\,dy = e^{-\lambda(r+t)}/e^{-\lambda t} = e^{-\lambda r} = $

$\displaystyle\int_{r}^{\infty} \lambda e^{-\lambda y}\,dy = P(y \ge r)$. The exponential probability function applied in this context assumes no wearout—no matter how long the bulb has already remained lit, $f(y)$ implies that it has the same probability of working for at least another r hours.

2.6.15 Let K_i be the event that the ith key tried opens the door, $i = 1, 2, \ldots, n$. Then $P(\text{door opens}$
first time with 3rd key$) = P(K_1^C \cap K_2^C \cap K_3) = P(K_1^C) \cdot P(K_2^C \mid K_1^C) \cdot P(K_3 \mid K_1^C \cap K_2^C) = $
$\dfrac{n-1}{2} \cdot \dfrac{n-2}{n-1} \cdot \dfrac{1}{n-2} = \dfrac{1}{n}$.

2.6.17 Let B be the event that the face (or sum of faces) equals 6. Let A_1 be the event that a Head comes up and A_2, the event that a Tail comes up. Then $P(B) = P(B|A_1)P(A_1) + P(B|A_2)P(A_2) = $
$\dfrac{1}{6} \cdot \dfrac{1}{2} + \dfrac{5}{36} \cdot \dfrac{1}{2} = 0.15$.

2.6.19 Let B be the event that a donation is received; let A_1, A_2, and A_3 denote the events that the call is placed to Belle Meade, Oak Hill, and Antioch, respectively. Then $P(B) = $
$\displaystyle\sum_{i=1}^{3} P(B|A_i)P(A_i) = (0.60)\cdot\dfrac{1000}{4000} + (0.55)\cdot\dfrac{1000}{4000} + (0.35)\cdot\dfrac{2000}{4000} = 0.46$.

2.6.21 Let B be the event that a red chip is ultimately drawn from Urn I. Let A_{RW}, for example, denote the event that a red is transferred from Urn I and a white is transferred from Urn II. Then $P(B) = P(B \mid A_{RR})P(A_{RR}) + P(B \mid A_{RW})P(A_{RW}) + P(B \mid A_{WR})P(A_{WR}) + P(B \mid A_{WW})P(A_{WW}) =$
$$\frac{3}{4}\left(\frac{3}{4} \cdot \frac{2}{4}\right) + \frac{2}{4}\left(\frac{3}{4} \cdot \frac{2}{4}\right) + 1\left(\frac{1}{4} \cdot \frac{2}{4}\right) + \frac{3}{4}\left(\frac{1}{4} \cdot \frac{2}{4}\right) = \frac{11}{16}.$$

2.6.23 The optimal allocation has 1 white chip in one urn and the other 19 chips (9 white and 10 black) in the other urn. Then $P(\text{white is drawn}) = 1 \cdot \frac{1}{2} + \frac{9}{19} \cdot \frac{1}{2} = 0.74.$

2.6.25 Since the identities of the six chips drawn are not known, their selection does not affect any probability associated with the seventh card (recall Example 2.6.8). Therefore, $P(\text{seventh card drawn is red}) = P(\text{first chip drawn is red}) = \frac{40}{100}.$

2.6.27 Let B denote the event that the chip drawn from Urn II is red; Let A_R and A_W denote the events that the chips transferred are red and white, respectively. Then
$$P(A_W \mid B) = \frac{P(B \mid A_W)P(A_W)}{P(B \mid A_R)P(A_R) + P(B \mid A_W)P(A_W)} = \frac{(2/4)(2/3)}{(3/4)(1/3) + (2/4)(2/3)} = \frac{4}{7}$$

2.6.29 If B is the event that the warning light flashes and A is the event that the oil pressure is low, then
$$P(A \mid B) = \frac{P(B \mid A)P(A)}{P(B \mid A)P(A) + P(B \mid A^C)P(A^C)} = \frac{(0.99)(0.10)}{(0.99)(0.10) + (0.02)(0.90)} = 0.85$$

2.6.31 Let B denote the event that Francesca passed, and let A_X and A_Y denote the events that she was enrolled in Professor X's section and Professor Y's section, respectively. Since $P(B \mid A_X) = 0.85$, $P(B \mid A_Y) = 0.60$, $P(A_X) = 0.4$, and $P(A_Y) = 0.6$,
$$P(A_X \mid B) = \frac{(0.85)(0.4)}{(0.85)(0.4) + (0.60)(0.6)} = 0.486$$

2.6.33 Let B denote the event that the alarm goes off. If A is the event that the house is being burglarized, $P(B \mid A) = 0.95$, $P(B \mid A^C) = \frac{5}{730}$, $P(A) = \frac{2}{10,000}$, and
$$P(A \mid B) = \frac{(0.95)(2/10,000)}{(0.95)(2/10,000) + (5/730)(9998/10,000)} = 0.027$$

2.6.35 Define B to be the event that Josh answers a randomly selected question correctly, and let A_1 and A_2 denote the events that he was 1) unprepared for the question and 2) prepared for the question, respectively. Then $P(B|A_1) = 0.20$, $P(B|A_2) = 1$, $P(A_2) = p$, $P(A_1) = 1 - p$, and

$$P(A_2|B) = 0.92 = \frac{P(B|A_2)P(A_2)}{P(B|A_1)P(A_1) + P(B|A_2)P(A_2)} = \frac{1 \cdot p}{(0.20)(1-p) + (1 \cdot p)}$$

which implies that $p = 0.70$ (meaning that Josh was prepared for $(0.70)(20) = 14$ of the questions).

Section 2.7

2.7.1 If A and B are mutually exclusive, $P(A|B) = 0 \neq P(A) > 0$. By definition, then, A and B are not independent.

2.7.3 Let x denote the number of black females hired. If race and sex are to be independent,

$$P(\text{black female}) = \frac{x}{120+x} \text{ must equal } P(\text{black}) \cdot P(\text{female}) = \left(\frac{30+x}{120+x}\right) \cdot \left(\frac{40+x}{120+x}\right), \text{ or}$$

equivalently, $(120 + x)x = (30 + x)(40 + x)$, which implies that $x = 24$.

2.7.5 11 [= 6 verifications of the form $P(A_i \cap A_j) = P(A_i) \cdot P(A_j)$ + 4 verifications of the form $P(A_i \cap A_j \cap A_k) = P(A_i) \cdot P(A_j) \cdot P(A_k)$ + 1 verification that $P(A_1 \cap A_2 \cap A_3 \cap A_4) = P(A_1) \cdot P(A_2) \cdot P(A_3) \cdot P(A_4)$].

2.7.7 $P(A \cap B \cap C) = 0$ (since the sum of two odd numbers is necessarily even) $\neq P(A) \cdot P(B) \cdot P(C) > 0$, so A, B, and C are not mutually independent. However, $P(A \cap B) = \frac{9}{36} =$

$P(A) \cdot P(B) = \frac{3}{6} \cdot \frac{3}{6}$, $P(A \cap C) = \frac{9}{36} = P(A) \cdot P(C) = \frac{3}{6} \cdot \frac{18}{36}$, and $P(B \cap C) = \frac{9}{36} = P(B) \cdot$

$P(C) = \frac{3}{6} \cdot \frac{18}{36}$, so A, B, and C are pairwise independent.

2.7.9 $P(\text{one face is twice the other face}) = P((1, 2), (2, 1), (2, 4), (4, 2), (3, 6), (6, 3)) = \frac{6}{36}$.

2.7.11 Let M_X and W_X denote the events that a husband has blood type X and his wife has blood type X, respectively. Then $P(\text{husband and wife have different blood types}) = 1 - P(\text{husband and wife have same blood type}) = 1 - P((M_A \cap W_A) \cup (M_B \cap W_B) \cup (M_{AB} \cap W_{AB}) \cup (M_O \cap W_O))$ $= 1 - [(0.40)(0.40) + (0.10)(0.10) + (0.05)(0.05) + (0.45)(0.45)] = 0.625$. The intersections here are mutually exclusive, and we are assuming that M_X and W_X are independent. The latter is reasonable because blood type is not a factor in the selection of a mate.

2.7.13 Let J and L denote the events that Jim and Sally, respectively, spot a hyphenation error. Given that $P(J) = 0.80$, $P(L) = 0.50$, and $P(J \cap L) = 0.40$, $P(\text{error is undetected}) = P((J \cup L)^C)$ $= 1 - P(J \cap L) = 1 - [0.80 + 0.50 - 0.40] = 0.10$. Events J and L are independent because $P(J \cap L) = 0.40 = P(J) \cdot P(L) = (0.80)(0.50)$.

2.7.15 Let M, L, and G be the events that a student passes the mathematics, language, and general knowledge tests, respectively. Then $P(M) = \dfrac{6175}{9500}$, $P(L) = \dfrac{7600}{9500}$, and $P(G) = \dfrac{8075}{9500}$.

P(student fails to qualify) = P(student fails at least one exam) = $1 - P$(student passes all three exams) = $1 - P(M \cap L \cap G) = 1 - P(M) \cdot P(L) \cdot P(G) = 0.56$.

2.7.17 Six equally-likely orderings are possible for any set of three distinct random numbers: $x_1 < x_2 < x_3$, $x_1 < x_3 < x_2$, $x_2 < x_1 < x_3$, $x_2 < x_3 < x_1$, $x_3 < x_1 < x_2$, and $x_3 < x_2 < x_1$. By inspection, $P(A) = \dfrac{2}{6}$, and $P(B) = \dfrac{1}{6}$, so $P(A \cap B) = P(A) \cdot P(B) = \dfrac{1}{18}$.

2.7.19 $P(A_1 \cup A_2 \cup \cdots \cup A_n) = \displaystyle\sum_{i=1}^{n} P(A_i) - \sum_{i<j} P(A_i)P(A_j) + \sum_{i<j<k} P(A_i)P(A_j)P(A_k) - \cdots$
$\pm P(A_1)P(A_2) \cdots P(A_n)$. If the A_i's are independent, their union can be more easily calculated using complements: $P(A_1 \cup A_2 \cup \cdots A_n) = 1 - P(A_1^C \cap A_2^C \cap \cdots \cap A_n^C) = 1 - P(A_1^C)P(A_2^C) \cdots P(A_n^C)$.

Section 2.8

2.8.1 Let A_i denote the event that the ith bulb is defective, $i = 1, 2, \ldots, 8$. Given that $P(A_i) = 0.05$, P(string will not work) = $1 - P$(string will work) = $1 - P(A_1^C \cap A_2^C \cap \cdots A_8^C) = 1 - P(A_1^C)P(A_2^C) \cdots P(A_8^C) = 1 - (0.95)^8 = 0.34$.

2.8.3 Let B be the event that no heads appear, and let A_i be the event that i coins are tossed, $i = 1, 2, \ldots, 6$. Then $P(B) = \displaystyle\sum_{i=1}^{6} P(B|A_i)P(A_i) = \dfrac{1}{2}\left(\dfrac{1}{6}\right) + \left(\dfrac{1}{2}\right)^2\left(\dfrac{1}{6}\right) + \ldots + \left(\dfrac{1}{2}\right)^6\left(\dfrac{1}{6}\right) = \dfrac{63}{384}$.

2.8.5 P(at least one red chip is drawn from at least one urn) = $1 - P$(all chips drawn are white) =
$1 - \left(\dfrac{4}{7}\right)^r \cdot \left(\dfrac{4}{7}\right)^r \cdots \left(\dfrac{4}{7}\right)^4 = 1 - \left(\dfrac{4}{7}\right)^{rm}$.

2.8.7 P(at least one double six in n throws) = $1 - P$(no double sixes in n throws) = $1 - \left(\dfrac{35}{36}\right)^n$. By trial and error, the smallest n for which P(at least one double six in n throws) exceeds 0.50 is 25 $[1 - \left(\dfrac{35}{36}\right)^{24} = 0.49$; $1 - \left(\dfrac{35}{36}\right)^{25} = 0.51]$.

2.8.9 Let A_H, A_T, B_H, B_T, C_H, and C_T denote the events that players A, B, and C throw heads and tails on individual tosses. Then $P(A \text{ throws first head}) = P(A_H \cup (A_T \cap B_T \cap C_T \cap A_H) \cup \cdots)$

$$= \frac{1}{2} + \frac{1}{2}\left(\frac{1}{8}\right) + \frac{1}{2}\left(\frac{1}{8}\right)^2 + \cdots = \frac{1}{2}\left(\frac{1}{1-1/8}\right) = \frac{4}{7}. \text{ Similarly, } P(B \text{ throws first head}) =$$

$$P(A_T \cap B_H) \cup (A_T \cap B_T \cap C_T \cap A_T \cap B_H) \cup \cdots = \frac{1}{4} + \frac{1}{4}\left(\frac{1}{8}\right) + \frac{1}{4}\left(\frac{1}{8}\right)^2 + \cdots = \frac{1}{4}\left(\frac{1}{1-1/8}\right) = \frac{2}{7}.$$

$$P(C \text{ throws first head}) = 1 - \frac{4}{7} - \frac{2}{7} = \frac{1}{7}.$$

2.8.11 The table on the left lists the different sequences of rolls that would result in your opponent landing 6 spaces from GO; the table on the right shows a similar analysis for landing 8 spaces from GO. Since $P(\text{lands 8 spaces}) = 0.166 > P(\text{lands 6 spaces}) = 0.147$, the house should be put on Vermont Avenue.

Ways to move 6 spaces	Probability	Ways to move 8 spaces	Probability
(2, 2, 2)	$(1/36)^3$	(2, 2, 2, 2)	$(1/36)^4$
(2, 4)	$(1/36)(3/36)$	(2, 2, 4)	$(1/36)^2(3/36)$
(4, 2)	$(1/36)(3/36)$	(2, 4, 2)	$(1/36)^2(3/36)$
(3, 3)	$(2/36)^2$	(4, 2, 2)	$(1/36)^2(3/36)$
(6)	$5/36$	(2, 3, 3)	$(1/36)(2/36)^2$
	$\overline{0.147}$	(3, 2, 3)	$(1/36)(2/36)^2$
		(3, 3, 2)	$(1/36)(2/36)^2$
		(3, 5)	$(2/36)(4/36)$
		(5, 3)	$(2/36)(4/36)$
		(2, 6)	$(1/36)(5/36)$
		(6, 2)	$(1/36)(5/36)$
		(4, 4)	$(3/36)^2$
		(8)	$5/36$
			$\overline{0.166}$

2.8.13 $P(B \mid A_1) = 1 - P(\text{all } m \text{ I-teams fail}) = 1 - (1-r)^m$; similarly, $P(B \mid A_2) = 1 - (1-r)^{n-m}$. From Theorem 2.6.1, $P(B) = [1 - (1-r)^m]p + [1 - (1-r)^{n-m}](1-p)$. Treating m as a continuous variable and differentiating $P(B)$ gives $\dfrac{dP(B)}{dm} = -p(1-r)^m \ln(1-r) + (1-p)(1-r)^{n-m} \cdot$

$\ln(1-r)$. Setting $\dfrac{dP(B)}{dm} = 0$ implies that $m = \dfrac{n}{2} + \dfrac{\ln[(1-p)/p]}{2\ln(1-r)}$.

Section 2.9

2.9.1 $2 \cdot 3 \cdot 2 \cdot 2 = 24$

2.9.3 $3 \cdot 3 \cdot 5 = 45$. Included will be aeu and cdx.

2.9.5
   a) $26^2 \cdot 10^4 = 6{,}760{,}000$
   b) $26^2 \cdot 10 \cdot 9 \cdot 9 \cdot 8 \cdot 7 = 3{,}407{,}040$
   c) The total number of plate *with* four zeros is $26 \cdot 26$, so the total number *not* having four zeros must be $26^2 \cdot 10^4 - 26^2 = 6{,}759{,}324$.

2.9.7 For each topping, the customer has 2 choices: "add" or "do not add." The eight available toppings, then, can produce a total of $2^8 = 256$ different hamburgers.

2.9.9 With 4 choices for the first digit, 1 for the third digit, 5 for the last digit, and 10 for each of the remaining six digits, the total number of admissible zip codes is $20,000,000 (= 4 \cdot 10^6 \cdot 1 \cdot 5)$.

2.9.11 3, because $4^2 < 20$ but $4^3 > 20$.

2.9.13 4, because $2^1 + 2^2 + 2^3 < 26$ but $2^1 + 2^2 + 2^3 + 2^4 \geq 26$. Note: This solution is different than the genetic code encryption asked for in Question 2.9.11 because the Morse code for a given letter does not have to be a fixed length.

2.9.15 $_6P_3 = 6 \cdot 5 \cdot 4 = 120$

2.9.17 $\log_{10}(30!) \doteq \log_{10}\left(\sqrt{2\pi}\right) + \left(30 + \dfrac{1}{2}\right)\log_{10}(30) - 30\log_{10}e = 32.42246$, which implies that $30! \doteq 10^{32.42246} = 2.645 \times 10^{32}$.

2.9.19 There are 2 choices for the first digit, 6 choices for the middle digit, and 5 choices for the last digit, so the number of admissible integers that can be formed from the digits 1 through 7 is $60 (= 2 \cdot 6 \cdot 5)$.

2.9.21 There are 4 different sets of three semesters in which the electives could be taken. For each of those sets, the electives can be selected and arranged in $_{10}P_3$ ways, which means that the number of possible schedules is $4 \cdot {}_{10}P_3$, or 2880.

2.9.23 a) For each of the $_4P_4$ orders in which the men can be killed off, the four women can be dispatched in $_4P_4$ ways as well, so the total number of admissible "plots" is $_4P_4 \cdot {}_4P_4 = 4! \cdot 4! = 576$.

b) $_7P_7 \cdot 1 = 5040$

2.9.25 Within each of the n families, members can be lined up in $_mP_m = m!$ ways. Since the n families can be permuted in $_nP_n = n!$ ways, the total number of admissible ways to arrange the nm people is $n! \cdot (m!)^n$.

2.9.27 By inspection, $_nP_1 = n$. Assume that $_nP_k = n(n-1) \cdots (n-k+1)$ is the number of ways to arrange k distinct objects without repetition. Notice that $n - k$ options would be available for a $(k+1)$st object added to the sequences. By the multiplication rule, the number of sequences of length $k + 1$ must be $n(n-1) \cdots (n-k+1)(n-k)$. But the latter is the formula for $_nP_{k+1}$.

2.9.29 By definition, $(n + 1)! = (n + 1) \cdot n!$; let $n = 0$.

2.9.31 If the first digit is a 4, the remaining six digits can be arranged in $\dfrac{6!}{3!(1!)^3} = 120$ ways; if the first digit is a 5, the remaining six digits can be arranged in $\dfrac{6!}{2!2!(1!)^2} = 180$ ways. The total number of admissible numbers, then, is $120 + 180 = 300$.

2.9.33 a) $4! \cdot 3! \cdot 3! = 864$

    b) $3! \cdot 4!3!3! = 5184$ (each of the 3! permutations of the three nationalities can generate 4!3!3! arrangements of the ten people in line)

    c) $10! = 3,628,800$

    d) $10!/4!3!3! = 4200$

2.9.35 $9!/2!3!1!3! = 5040$ (recall Example 2.9.13)

2.9.37 Each path between any two points can be represented as a permutation. For example, any admissible path from X to O consists of 9 steps "to the right" and 2 steps "up." By the multiplication rule, the number of admissible paths from X to Y through O = number of admissible paths from X to O times the number of admissible paths from O to Y $= \dfrac{11!}{9!2!} \cdot \dfrac{8!}{5!3!} = 3080.$

2.9.39 Imagine a field of 4 entrants (A, B, C, D) assigned to positions 1 through 4, where positions 1 and 2 correspond to the opponents for game 1 and positions 3 and 4 correspond to the opponents for game 2. Although the four players can be assigned to the four positions in 4! ways, not all of those permutations yield different tournaments. For example, $\dfrac{B\ C\ A\ D}{1\ 2\ 3\ 4}$ and $\dfrac{A\ D\ B\ C}{1\ 2\ 3\ 4}$ produce the same set of games, as do $\dfrac{B\ C\ A\ D}{1\ 2\ 3\ 4}$ and $\dfrac{C\ B\ A\ D}{1\ 2\ 3\ 4}$. In general, n games can be arranged in $n!$ ways, and the two players in each game can be permuted in 2! ways. Given a field of $2n$ entrants, then, the number of distinct pairings is $(2n)!/n!(2!)^n$, or $1 \cdot 3 \cdot 5 \cdots (2n - 1)$.

2.9.41 The letters in E L E E M O S Y N A R Y minus the pair S Y can be permuted in 10!/3! ways. Since S Y can be positioned in front of, within, or behind those ten letters in 11 ways, the number of admissible arrangements is $11 \cdot 10!/3! = 6,652,800$.

2.9.43 Consider $k!$ objects categorized into $(k - 1)!$ groups, each group being of size k. By Theorem 2.9.2, the number of ways to arrange the $k!$ objects is $(k!)!/(k!)^{(k-1)!}$, but the latter must be an integer.

2.9.45 Since every (unordered) set of two letters describes a different line, the number of possible lines is $\binom{5}{2} = 10$.

2.9.47 Of the eight crew members, five need to be on a given side of the boat. Clearly, the remaining three can be assigned to the sides in 3 ways. Moreover, the rowers on each side can be permuted in 4! ways. By the multiplication rule, then, the number of ways to arrange the crew is $1728 (= 3 \cdot 4! \cdot 4!)$.

2.9.49 $\binom{7}{5} = 21$; order does not matter.

2.9.51 Imagine arranging the E's and the P's without the M's. In order for the methyls to be nonadjacent they must occupy one of the $\binom{16}{6}$ sets of spaces between and around the fifteen E's and P's. By Theorem 2.9.2, the latter can be arranged in $\dfrac{15!}{10!5!}$ ways, so the total number of admissible chains is $\binom{16}{6} \cdot \dfrac{15!}{10!5!} = 24{,}048{,}024.$

2.9.53 Let $x = y = 1$ in the expansion $(x+ y)^n = \sum\limits_{k=0}^{n} \binom{n}{k} x^k y^{n-k}$. The total number of hamburgers referred to in Question 2.9.7 ($= 2^8$) must also be equal to the number of ways to choose k condiments, $k = 0, 1, 2, \ldots, 8$—that is, $\binom{8}{0} + \binom{8}{1} + \ldots + \binom{8}{8}$.

2.9.55 Let $x = y = 1$ in the expansion $(x - y)^n = \sum\limits_{k=0}^{n} \binom{n}{k} x^k (-y)^{n-k}$. Then $x - y = 0$ and the sum reduces to $0 = \sum\limits_{k=0}^{n} \binom{n}{k} (-1)^{n-k}$, or equivalently, $\binom{n}{1} + \binom{n}{3} + \ldots = \binom{n}{0} + \binom{n}{2} + \ldots$.

2.9.57 When n is even, $\binom{n}{j}$ is maximized when $j = \dfrac{n}{2}$ (see Question 2.9.56). Therefore, entropy is maximized when $\dfrac{n}{2}$ molecules are present in each chamber.

2.9.59 If no ties occur, the horses can finish in 5! ways. Any of two horses could tie for positions 1 and 2, 2 and 3, 3 and 4, or 4 and 5. The remaining three horses could then be permuted in 3! ways. It follows that the total number of possible finishes must be $5! + 4 \cdot \binom{5}{2} \cdot 3! = 360.$

Section 2.10

2.10.1 $\dbinom{7}{2}\dbinom{3}{2} \Big/ \dbinom{10}{4}$

2.10.3 $P(\text{numbers differ by more than 2}) = 1 - P(\text{numbers differ by one}) - P(\text{numbers differ by 2}) = 1 - 19\Big/\dbinom{20}{2} - 18\Big/\dbinom{20}{2} = \dfrac{153}{190} = 0.81.$

2.10.5 Let A_1 be the event that an urn with $3W$ and $3R$ is sampled; let A_2 be the event that the urn with $5W$ and $1R$ is sampled. Let B be the event that the three chips drawn are white. By Bayes' rule,

$$P(A_2|B) = \frac{P(B|A_2)P(A_2)}{P(B|A_1)P(A_1) + P(B|A_2)P(A_2)}$$

$$= \frac{\left[\binom{5}{3}\binom{1}{0}\middle/\binom{6}{3}\right]\cdot(1/10)}{\left[\binom{3}{3}\binom{3}{0}\middle/\binom{6}{3}\right]\cdot(9/10)+\left[\binom{5}{3}\binom{1}{0}\middle/\binom{6}{3}\right]\cdot(1/10)} = \frac{10}{19}$$

2.10.7 $6/6^n = 1/6^{n-1}$

2.10.9 By Theorem, 2.9.2, the $2n$ grains of sand can be arranged in $(2n)!/n!n!$ ways. Two of those arrangements have the property that the colors will completely separate. Therefore, the probability of the latter is $2(n!)^2/(2n)!$.

2.10.11 $P(\text{different floors}) = 7!/7^7$; $P(\text{same floor}) = 7/7^7 = 1/7^6$. The assumption being made is that all possible departure patterns are equally likely, which is probably not true, since residents living on lower floors would be less inclined to wait for the elevator than would those living on the top floors.

2.10.13 The 10 short pieces and 10 long pieces can be lined up in a row in $20!/(10)!(10)!$ ways. Consider each of the 10 pairs of consecutive pieces as defining the reconstructed sticks. Each of those pairs could combine a short piece (S) and a long piece (L) in two ways: SL or LS. Therefore, the number of permutations that would produce 10 sticks, each having a short and a long component is 2^{10}, so the desired probability is $2^{10}\middle/\binom{20}{10}$.

2.10.15 Any of $\binom{k}{2}$ people could share any of 365 possible birthdays. The remaining $k-2$ people can generate $364 \cdot 363 \cdots (365 - k + 2)$ sequences of distinct birthdays. Therefore, $P(\text{exactly one match}) = \binom{k}{2} \cdot 365 \cdot 364 \cdots (365 - k + 2)/365^k$.

2.10.17 To get a flush, Dana needs to draw any three of the remaining eleven diamonds. Since only forty-seven cards are effectively left in the deck (others may already have been dealt, but their identities are unknown), $P(\text{Dana draws to flush}) = \binom{11}{3}\middle/\binom{47}{3}$.

2.10.19 There are two pairs of cards that would give Tim a straight flush (5 of clubs and 7 of clubs or 7 of clubs and 10 of clubs). Therefore, $P(\text{Tim draws to straight flush}) = 2\middle/\binom{47}{2}$. A flush, by definition, consists of five cards in the same suit whose denominations are not all consecutive. It follows that $P(\text{Tim draws to flush}) = \left[\binom{10}{2}-2\right]\middle/\binom{47}{2}$, where the "2" refers to the straight flushes cited earlier.

2.10.21 $\binom{5}{3}\binom{4}{2}^3\binom{3}{1}\binom{4}{2}\binom{2}{1}\binom{4}{1} \Big/ \binom{52}{9}$

2.10.23 $\left[\binom{2}{1}\binom{2}{1}\right]^4 \binom{32}{4} \Big/ \binom{48}{12}$

Chapter 3

Section 3.2

3.2.1   Each outcome has probability 1/10

Outcome	X = larger no. drawn
1, 2	2
1, 3	3
1, 4	4
1, 5	5
2, 3	3
2, 4	4
2, 5	5
3, 4	4
3, 5	5
4, 5	5

Counting the number of each value of the larger of the two and multiplying by 1/10 gives the pdf:

k	$p_X(k)$
2	1/10
3	2/10
4	3/10
5	4/10

3.2.3   There are 18 words and each is equally likely to be chosen. Then the non-zero values of $p_X(k)$ are:

$$p_X(1) = P(a) = 1/18$$
$$p_X(2) = P(\text{of, to, is, on}) = 4/18$$
$$p_X(3) = P(\text{The, has, but, way, and, the, the}) = 7/18$$
$$p_X(4) = P(\text{Bird, Time, Bird, wing}) = 4/18$$
$$p_X(6) = P(\text{little}) = 1/18$$
$$p_X(7) = P(\text{flutter}) = 1/18$$

3.2.5   Let us consider the case $k = 0$, as an example. If you are on the left, with your friend on your immediate right, you and stand in positions 1, 2, 3, or 4. The remaining people can stand in 3! ways. Each of these must be multiplied by 2, since your friend could be the one on the left. The total number of permutations of the five people is 5!
Thus,

$$p_X(0) = (2)(4)(3!)/5! = 48/120 = 4/10$$

In a similar manner

$$p_X(1) = (2)(3)(3!)/5! = 36/120 = 3/10$$
$$p_X(2) = (2)(2)(3!)/5! = 24/120 = 2/10$$
$$p_X(3) = (2)(1)(3!)/5! = 12/120 = 1/10$$

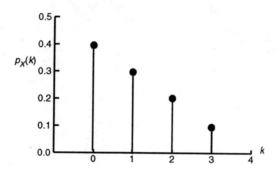

3.2.7 $p_X(k) = \dfrac{\dbinom{4}{k}\dbinom{48}{5-k}}{\dbinom{52}{5}}$ $k = 0, 1, 2, 3, 4$

3.2.9 $p_{X_1}(k) = p_{X_2}(k) = \dfrac{\dbinom{2}{k}\dbinom{2}{2-k}}{\dbinom{4}{2}}$, $k = 0, 1, 2$. For $X_1 + X_2 = m$, let

$X_1 = k$ and $X_2 = m - k$, for $k = 0, 1, \ldots, m$. Then $p_{X_3}(m) = \displaystyle\sum_{k=0}^{m} p_{X_1}(k)p_{X_2}(m-k)$,

$m = 0, 1, 2, 3, 4$, or

m	$P_{X_3}(m)$
0	1/36
1	2/9
2	1/2
3	2/9
4	1/36

3.2.11 $\quad P\left(\left|Y - \frac{1}{2}\right| > \frac{1}{4}\right) = P\left(Y < \frac{1}{4}\right) + P\left(Y > \frac{3}{4}\right)$

$$= \int_0^{1/4} 3(1-y)^2 \, dy + \int_{3/4}^1 3(1-y)^2 \, dy$$

$$= -(1-y)^3 \Big|_0^{1/4} - (1-y)^3 \Big|_{3/4}^1 = -(3/4)^3 + 1 - 0 + (1/4)^3$$

$$= -27/64 + 1 + 1/64 = 38/64$$

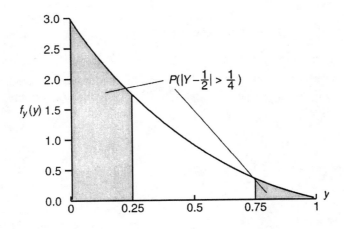

Section 3.3

3.3.1 The probability of the appearance of discrimination is P(all men) + P(all women)

$$= \frac{\binom{5}{3}\binom{4}{0}}{\binom{9}{3}} + \frac{\binom{5}{0}\binom{4}{3}}{\binom{9}{3}} = 14/84$$

3.3.3 The random variable X is hypergeometric with $N = 4050$, $n = 65$, $r = 514$, and $w = 4050 - 514 = 3536$. Thus,

$$p_X(k) = \frac{\binom{514}{k}\binom{3536}{65-k}}{\binom{4050}{65}}, \, k = 0, 1, 2, \dots, 65$$

3.3.5 Let X be a hypergeometric random variable with $N = 10$, $n = 5$, $r = 8$, and $w = 10 - 8 = 2$. Then k will be the number of questions chosen that Anne has studied. The probability of her getting at least 4 correct is

$$p_X(4) + p_X(5) = \frac{\binom{8}{4}\binom{2}{1}}{\binom{10}{5}} + \frac{\binom{8}{5}\binom{2}{0}}{\binom{10}{5}} = \frac{140}{252} + \frac{56}{252} = 0.778$$

Anne's strategy does not yield the desired 85% chance of getting at least four of the five questions correct.

3.3.7 After three drawings, the probability of the next chip being one of your numbers is 2/37. The probability that the final chip is your remaining number is 1/36. The probability of winning is $(2/37)(1/36) = 2/1332 = 0.0015$.

3.3.9
$$\frac{\binom{2}{2}\binom{8}{0} + \binom{6}{2}\binom{4}{0} + \binom{2}{2}\binom{8}{0}}{\binom{10}{2}} = \frac{1 + 15 + 1}{45} = \frac{17}{45} = 0.378$$

3.3.11 There are $\binom{N}{n}$ total ways to chose the sample. There are $\binom{n_i}{k_i}$ ways to arrange for k_i of the n_i objects to be chosen, for each i. Using the multiplication rule shows that

$$P(X_1 = k_1, X_2 = k_2, \ldots, X_t = k_t) = \frac{\binom{n_1}{k_1}\binom{n_2}{k_2}\cdots\binom{n_t}{k_t}}{\binom{N}{n}}$$

3.3.13 For any value of $r =$ number of defective items, the probability of accepting the sample is
$$p_r = \frac{\binom{r}{0}\binom{100-r}{10}}{\binom{100}{10}} + \frac{\binom{r}{1}\binom{100-r}{9}}{\binom{100}{10}}$$

Then the operating characteristic curve is the plot of the presumed percent defective versus the probability of accepting the shipment, or $100(r/100) = r$ on the x-axis and p_r on the y-axis. If there are 16 defective, you will accept the shipment approximately 50% of the time.

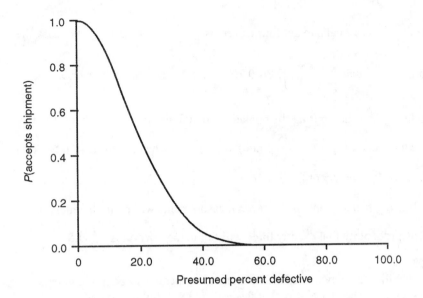

3.3.15 Let X = the number of control rods properly inserted. Then X is binomial with $n = 10$ and $p = 0.80$. The system fails when $X \le 4$. The probability of failure is

$$P(X \le 4) = \sum_{k=0}^{4} \binom{10}{k}(0.8)^k(0.2)^{10-k} = 0.0064$$

3.3.17 Let X_1 = the number of bulbs in system 1 that burn out in 30 days. Then X_1 is binomial with $n = 50$ and $p = 0.05$.

$$P(X_1 \ge 1) = 1 - P(X_1 = 0) = 1 - (0.95)^{50} = 1 - 0.077 = 0.923$$

Let X_2 = the number of bulbs in system 2 that burn out in 30 days. Then X_2 is binomial with $n = 100$ and $p = 0.02$.

$$P(X_2 \ge 1) = 1 - P(X_2 = 0) = 1 - (0.98)^{100} = 1 - 0.133 = 0.867$$

System 2 is superior from a bulb replacement perspective.

3.3.19 Let X_1 = the number of missile hits on the plane. Then X_1 is binomial with $n = 6$ and $p = 0.2$. The probability the plane will crash is $P(X_1 \ge 2) = 1 - P(X_1 = 0) - P(X_1 = 1) = 1 - (0.8)^6 - 6(0.2)(0.8)^5 = 1 - 0.262 - 0.393 = 0.345$.

Let X_2 = the number of rocket hits on the plane. Then X_2 is binomial with $n = 10$ and $p = 0.05$. The probability the boat will be disabled is $P(X_2 \ge 1) = 1 - P(X_2 = 0) = 1 - (0.95)^{10} = 1 - 0.599 = 0.401$.

3.3.21 Let X = the number of girls; then X is binomial with $n = 4$ and $p = 1/2$. The probability of two girls and two boys is $\binom{4}{2}0.5^4 = 0.375$. The probability of three and one is $2\binom{4}{3}0.5^4 = 0.5$, so the latter is more likely.

3.3.23 The probability it takes k calls to get four drivers is $\binom{k-1}{3}0.80^4 0.20^{k-4}$. We seek the smallest number n so that $\sum_{k=4}^{n}\binom{k-1}{3}0.80^4 0.20^{k-4} \geq 0.95$. By trial and error, $n = 7$.

3.3.25 The probability of any shell hitting the bunker is $30/500 = 0.06$. The probability of exactly k shells hitting the bunker is $p(k) = \binom{25}{k}(0.06)^k (0.94)^{25-k}$. The probability the bunker is destroyed is $1 - p(0) - p(1) - p(2) = 0.187$.

3.3.27 1) The probability that any one of the seven measurements will be in the interval $(1/2, 1)$ is 0.50. The probability that exactly three will fall in the interval is $\binom{7}{3}0.5^7$

$= 0.273$

2) The probability that any one of the seven measurements will be in the interval $(3/4, 1)$ is 0.25. The probability that fewer than 3 will fall in the interval is

$$\sum_{k=0}^{2}\binom{7}{k}(0.25)^k (0.75)^{7-k} = 0.756$$

3.3.29 Any particular sequence having k_1 of Outcome 1 and k_2 of Outcome 2, must have $n - k_1 - k_2$ of Outcome 3. The probability of such a sequence is $p_1^{k_1} p_2^{k_2}(1 - p_2 - p_2)^{n-k_1-k_2}$

The number of such sequences depends on the number of ways to choose the k_1 positions in the sequence for Outcome 1 and the k_2 positions for Outcome 2. The k_1 positions can be chosen in $\binom{n}{k_1}$ ways. For each such choice, the k_2 positions can be chosen in $\binom{n-k_1}{k_2}$ ways. Thus, $P(X_1 = k_1$ and $X_2 = k_2) =$

$$\binom{n}{k_1}\binom{n-k_1}{k_2}p_1^{k_1} p_1^{k_2}(1 - p_1 - p_2)^{n-k_1-k_2}$$

$$= \frac{n!}{k_1!(n-k_1)!}\frac{(n-k_1)!}{k_2!(n-k_1-k_2)!}p_1^{k_1} p_2^{k_2}(1 - p_1 - p_2)^{n-k_1-k_2}$$

$$= \frac{n!}{k_1! k_2!(n-k_1-k_2)!}p_1^{k_1} p_2^{k_2}(1 - p_1 - p_2)^{n-k_1-k_2}$$

3.3.31 The probability that any one of the robots is still working after 5 hours is $\int_{5}^{\infty}(1/\theta)e^{-x/\theta}dx = e^{-5/\theta}$. The probability that exactly r robots will be working is $\binom{n}{r}(e^{-5/\theta})^r (1 - e^{-5/\theta})^{n-r}$

Section 3.4

3.4.1   For $x < 1$, $F_X(x) = 0$
For $1 \le x < 2$, $F_X(x) = 1/3$
For $2 \le x < 3$, $F_X(x) = 1/3 + 1/3 = 2/3$
For $3 < x$, $F_X(x) = 1$

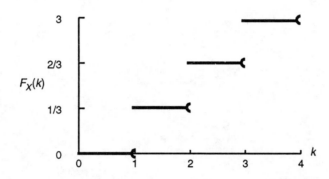

3.4.3   For $y < 0$, $F_Y(y) = 0$.

For $0 \le y < 1$, $F_Y(y) = \int_0^y 3t(1-t)dt = \frac{3}{2}y^2 - y^3$

For $1 \le y < 2$, $F_Y(y) = 1/2$

For $2 \le y < 3$, $F_Y(y) = \int_0^y 1/2 \, dt = \frac{1}{2}y - \frac{1}{2}$

For $y \ge 3$, $F_Y(y) = 1$

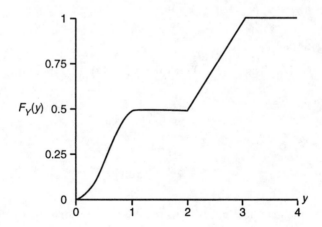

3.4.5   For $-5 \le y \le 5$, $F_Y(y) = \int_{-5}^y \frac{1}{10}dt = \frac{y+5}{10}$. Then $\frac{y+5}{10} = 0.60$ if $y = 1$.

3.4.7 $f_X(k) = ck$, $k = 1, 2, 3, 4$, and some constant c. But $1 = \sum_{k=1}^{4} f_X(k) = \sum_{k=1}^{4} ck = c + 2c + 3c + 4c$

$= 10c$, so $c = 0.1$. $f_X(k) = (0.1)k$, $k = 1, 2, 3, 4$

$$F_X(x) = \begin{cases} 0 & x < 1 \\ 0.10 & 1 \le x < 2 \\ 0.30 & 2 \le x < 3 \\ 0.60 & 3 \le x < 4 \\ 1 & 4 \le x \end{cases}$$

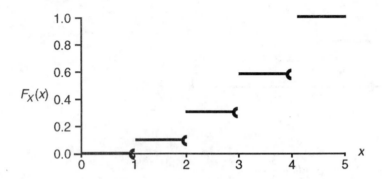

3.4.9 $0.57 = F_Y(3) - F_Y(2) = P(Y \le 3) - P(Y \le 2) = P(2 < Y \le 3)$

3.4.11 $P(-a < Y < a) = P(-a < Y \le 0) + P(0 < Y < a)$

$= \int_{-a}^{0} f_Y(y)dy + \int_0^a f_Y(y)dy = -\int_a^0 f_Y(-y)dy + \int_0^a f_Y(y)dy$

$= \int_0^a f_Y(y)dy + \int_0^a f_Y(y)dy = 2[F_Y(a) - F_Y(0)]$

But by the symmetry of f_Y, $F_Y(0) = 1/2$. Thus, $2[F_Y(a) - F_Y(0)] = 2[F_Y(a) - 1/2] = 2F_Y(a) - 1$

3.4.13 Choose an element a in A, and take $B = A - \{a\}$, $C = \{a\}$.

3.4.15 $F_Y(y) = \int_0^y (1/\lambda)e^{-t/\lambda} dt = 1 - e^{-t/\lambda}$, so

$h(y) = \dfrac{(1/\lambda)e^{-y/\lambda}}{1 - (1 - e^{-y/\lambda})} = 1/\lambda$

Since the hazard rate is constant, the item does not age. Its reliability does not decrease over time.

3.4.17 $P(1 \le e^Y \le 2) = P(\ln 1 \le Y \le \ln 2) = F_Y(\ln 2) - F_Y(0) = (1 - e^{-\ln 2}) - 0 = 1 - 1/2 = 1/2$

3.4.19 The random variable X is binomial, with $n = 10$. If the new therapy has no effect, then

$p = 0.30$. The quantity $1 - F_X(7) = P(X > 7) = \sum_{k=8}^{10} \binom{10}{k}(0.3)^k (0.7)^{10-k} = 0.00159$

The small probability of seeing 8 or more cures argues against the hypothesis that the medicine has no effect.

Section 3.5

3.5.1 $1 = \sum_{x,y} p(x,y) = c \sum_{x,y} xy =$

$c[(1)(1) + (2)(1) + (2)(2) + (3)(1)] = 10c$, so $c = 1/10$

3.5.3 $1 = \int_0^1 \int_0^y c(x+y)dxdy = c \int_0^1 \left[\frac{x^2}{2} + xy \right]_0^y dy$

$$= c \int_0^1 \frac{3y^2}{2} dy = c \left[\frac{y^3}{2} \right]_0^1 = \frac{c}{2}, \text{ so } c = 2.$$

3.5.5 $P(X = x, Y = y) = \dfrac{\binom{3}{x}\binom{2}{y}\binom{4}{3-x-y}}{\binom{9}{3}}, x \le 3, y \le 2, x+y \le 3$

3.5.7 $P(X > Y) = p_{X,Y}(1, 0) + p_{X,Y}(2, 0) + p_{X,Y}(2, 1)$
$= 6/50 + 4/50 + 3/50 = 13/50$

3.5.9   (a) $1 = \int_0^1 \int_0^1 c\, dxdy = c$, so $c = 1$

      (b) $P(0 < X < 1/2), 0 < Y < 1/4) = \int_0^{1/4} \int_0^{1/2} 1\, dxdy = 1/8$

3.5.11 The density is the bivariate uniform over a circle of radius 2. The area of the circle is $\pi(2)^2 = 4\pi$. Thus, $f_{X,Y}(x, y) = 1/4\pi$.

3.5.13 The probability of an observation falling into the interval $(0, 1/3)$ is $\int_0^{1/3} 2t\, dt = 1/9$. The probability of an observation falling into the interval $(1/3, 2/3)$ is $\int_{1/3}^{2/3} 2t\, dt = 1/3$. Assume without any loss of generality that the five observations are done in order. To calculate $p_{X,Y}(1, 2)$, note that there are $\binom{5}{1}$ places where the observation in $(0, 1/3)$ could occur, and $\binom{4}{2}$ choices for the location of the observations in $(1/3, 2/3)$. Then

$$p_{X,Y}(1, 2) = \binom{5}{1}\binom{4}{2}(1/9)^1 (1/3)^2 (5/9)^2 = 750/6561$$

3.5.15 (a) $S = \{(H, 1), (H, 2), (H, 3), (H, 4), (H, 5), (H, 6), (T, 1), (T, 2), (T, 3), (T, 4), (T, 5), (T, 6)\}$

      (b) $F_{X,Y}(1, 2) = P(X \le 1, Y \le 2)$
$= P(\{(H, 1), (H, 2), (T, 1), (T, 2)\}) = 4/12 = 1/3$

3.5.17 $F_{X,Y} = \begin{cases} = & 0, & 0 \le x < 5, \text{ any } y \\ = 1/2, & 5 \le x < 6, 2 \le y < 3 \\ = 2/3, & 5 \le x < 6, 3 \le y \\ = 2/3, & 6 \le x, 2 \le y < 3 \\ = & 1, & 6 \le x, 3 \le y \end{cases}$

3.5.19 By Theorem 3.5.1, $f_{X,Y} = \dfrac{\partial^2}{\partial x \partial y} F_{X,Y} = \dfrac{\partial^2}{\partial x \partial y}(xy) = \dfrac{\partial}{\partial x}\left(\dfrac{\partial}{\partial y} xy \right)$

$= \dfrac{\partial}{\partial x}(x) = 1, 0 < x < 1, 0 < y < 1.$

The graph of $f_{X,Y}$ is a plane of height one over the unit square.

3.5.21 First note that $1 = F_{X,Y}(1, 1) = k[4(1^2)(1^2) + 5(1)(1^4)] = 9k$, so $k = 1/9$.

Then $f_{X,Y} = \dfrac{\partial^2}{\partial x \partial y} F_{X,Y} = \dfrac{\partial^2}{\partial x \partial y}\left(\dfrac{4}{9}x^2 y^2 + \dfrac{5}{9}xy^4 \right)$

$= \dfrac{\partial}{\partial x} \dfrac{\partial}{\partial y}\left(\dfrac{4}{9}x^2 y^2 + \dfrac{5}{9}xy^4 \right) = \dfrac{\partial}{\partial x}\left(\dfrac{8}{9}x^2 y + \dfrac{20}{9}xy^3 \right) = \dfrac{16}{9}xy + \dfrac{20}{9}y^3$

$P(0 < X < 1/2, 1/2 < Y < 1) = \displaystyle\int_0^{1/2} \int_{1/2}^1 \left(\dfrac{16}{9}xy + \dfrac{20}{9}y^3 \right) dy\,dx$

$= \displaystyle\int_0^{1/2} \dfrac{8}{9}xy^2 + \dfrac{5}{9}y^4 \Big|_{1/2}^1 dx = \int_0^{1/2} \left(\dfrac{2}{3}x + \dfrac{25}{48} \right) dx$

$= \dfrac{1}{3}x^2 + \dfrac{25}{48}x \Big|_0^{1/2} = 11/32$

3.5.23 $f_X(x) = \displaystyle\int_{-\infty}^\infty f_{X,Y}(x, y)\,dy = \int_0^{1-x} 6x\,dy = 6xy \Big|_0^{1-x}$

$= 6x(1 - x), 0 < x < 1$

$f_Y(y) = \displaystyle\int_{-\infty}^\infty f_{X,Y}(x,y)\,dx = \int_0^{1-y} 6x\,dx = 3x^2 \Big|_0^{1-y}$

$= 3(1 - y)^2, 0 < y < 1$

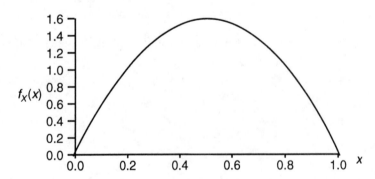

3.5.25 $f_X(x) = \int_x^2 \frac{1}{2} dy = \frac{y}{2}\Big|_x^2 = 1 - \frac{x}{2}, \, 0 < x < 2$

3.5.27 $f_Y(y) = \int_0^y 2e^{-x}e^{-y}dx = -2e^{-x}e^{-y}\Big|_0^y = 2e^{-y} - 2e^{-2y}, \, 0 < y$

3.5.29 $P(X_1 \geq 1050, X_2 \geq 1050, X_3 \geq 1050, X_4 \geq 1050)$

$$= \int_{1050}^\infty \int_{1050}^\infty \int_{1050}^\infty \int_{1050}^\infty \prod_{i=1}^4 \frac{1}{1000} e^{-x_i/1000} dx_1 dx_2 dx_3 dx_4$$

$$= \left(\int_{1050}^\infty \frac{1}{1000} e^{-x/1000} dx \right)^4 = (e^{1.05})^4 = 0.015$$

3.5.31 $p_{X,Y}(0, 1) = \sum_{z=0}^2 p_{X,Y,Z}(0,1,z)$

$$= \frac{3!}{0!\,1!} \left(\frac{1}{2}\right)^0 \left(\frac{1}{12}\right)^1 \sum_{z=0}^2 \frac{1}{z!(2-z)!}\left(\frac{1}{6}\right)^z\left(\frac{1}{4}\right)^{2-z}$$

$$= \frac{3!}{0!\,1!} \left(\frac{1}{2}\right)^0 \left(\frac{1}{12}\right)^1 \left(\frac{1}{2}\right) \sum_{z=0}^2 \frac{2!}{z!(2-z)!}\left(\frac{1}{6}\right)^z\left(\frac{1}{4}\right)^{2-z}$$

$$= \frac{3!}{0!\,1!} \left(\frac{1}{2}\right)^0 \left(\frac{1}{12}\right)^1 \left(\frac{1}{2}\right)\left(\frac{1}{6}+\frac{1}{4}\right)^2 = \frac{25}{576}$$

3.5.33 $f_{W,X}(w, x) = \int_0^1 \int_0^1 f_{W,X,Y,Z}(w,x,y,z) dy dz = \int_0^1 \int_0^1 16wxyz \, dy dz$

$$= \int_0^1 \left[8wxy^2 z\right]_0^1 dz = \int_0^1 [8wxz]dz = \left[4wxz^2\right]_0^1 = 4wx, \, 0 < w, x < 1$$

$P(0 < W < 1/2, 1/2, < X < 1) = \int_0^{1/2} \int_{1/2}^1 4wx \, dx dw$

$$= \int_0^{1/2} 2w\left[x^2\right]_{1/2}^1 dx = \int_0^{1/2} \frac{3}{2} w \, dw = \frac{3}{4} w^2 \Big|_0^{1/2} = \frac{3}{16}$$

Section 3.6

3.6.1 We must show that $p_{X,Y}(j,k) = p_X(j)p_Y(k)$. But for any pair (j, k), $p_{X,Y}(j,k) = 1/36 = (1/6)(1/6)$ $= p_X(j)p_Y(k)$.

3.6.3 First, note $k = 2$. Then, 2 times area of $A = P(Y \geq 3/4)$. Also, 2 times area of $B = P(X \geq 3/4)$. The square C is the set $(X \geq 3/4) \cap (Y \geq 3/4)$. However, C is in the region where the density is 0. Thus, $P((X \geq 3/4) \cap (Y \geq 3/4))$ is zero, but the product $P(X \geq 3/4)P(Y \geq 3/4)$ is not zero.

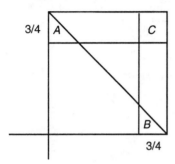

3.6.5 $\displaystyle P(Y < X) = \int_0^1 \int_0^x f_{X,Y}(x,y)\, dy\,dx = \int_0^1 \int_0^x (2x)(3y^2)\, dy\,dx = \int_0^1 2x^4\, dx = \frac{2}{5}$

3.6.7 $\displaystyle P\left(\frac{Y}{X} > 2\right) = P(Y > 2X) = \int_0^1 \int_0^{y/2} (2x)(1)\,dx\,dy = \int_0^1 \left[x^2\right]_0^{y/2} dy = \left.\frac{y^3}{12}\right|_0^1 = \frac{1}{12}$

3.6.9 Take $a = c = 0$, $b = d = 1/2$. Then
$$P(0 < X < 1/2, 0 < Y < 1/2) = \int_0^{1/2} \int_0^{1/2} (2x + y - 2xy)\,dy\,dx = 5/32.$$

$\displaystyle f_X(x) = \int_0^1 (2x + y - 2xy)\,dy = x + 1/2$, so $\displaystyle P(0 < X < 1/2) = \int_0^{1/2} \left(x + \frac{1}{2}\right) dx = \frac{3}{8}$

$\displaystyle f_Y(y) = \int_0^1 (2x + y - 2xy)\,dx = 1$, so $P(0 < X < 1/2) = 1/2$. But, $5/32 \neq (3/8)(1/2)$

3.6.11 Let K be the region of the plane where $f_{X,Y} \neq 0$. If K is not a rectangle with sides parallel to the coordinate axes, there exists a rectangle
$$A = \{(x, y) \mid a \leq x \leq b, c \leq y \leq d\}$$
with $A \cap K = \emptyset$, but for $A_1 = \{(x, y) \mid a \leq x \leq b, \text{ all } y\}$ and $A_2 = \{(x, y) \mid \text{ all } x, c \leq y \leq d\}$, $A_1 \cap K \neq \emptyset$ and $A_2 \cap K \neq \emptyset$. Then $P(A) = 0$, but $P(A_1) \neq 0$ and $P(A_2) \neq 0$. However, $A = A_1 \cap A_2$, so $P(A_1 \cap A_2) \neq P(A_1)P(A_2)$.

3.6.13 (a) $\displaystyle P(X_1 < 1/2) = \int_0^{1/2} 4x^3\,dx = \left.x^4\right|_0^{1/2} = 1/16$

(b) This asks for the probability of exactly one success in a binomial experiment with $n = 4$ and $p = 1/16$. So the probability is $\dbinom{4}{1}(1/16)^1(15/16)^3 = 0.206$.

(c) $f_{X_1,X_2,X_3X_4}(x_1,x_2,x_3,x_4) = \prod_{j=1}^{4} 4x_j^3 = 256(x_1x_2x_3x_4)^3$

(d) $F_{X_2,X_3}(x_2,x_3) = \int_0^{x_3}\int_0^{x_2}(4s^3)(4t^3)dsdt = \int_0^{x_2} 4s^2 ds \int_0^{x_3} 4t^3 dt = x_2^4 x_3^4,\ 0 \le x_2, x_3 \le 1.$

Section 3.7

3.7.1 $p_Y(y) = P(Y = y) = P(2X - 1 = y) = P\left(X = \dfrac{1}{2}y + \dfrac{1}{2}\right)$, so

$$p_Y(y) = \frac{\dbinom{4}{\frac{1}{2}y + \frac{1}{2}}\dbinom{3}{-\frac{1}{2}y + \frac{3}{2}}}{\dbinom{7}{2}},\ y = -1,\ 1,\ 3$$

3.7.3 Since $0 \le X \le 1$, $-3(0) - 4 \ge Y > -3(1) - 4$, or $-7 \le Y \le -4$.

If X is uniform, so is Y. Thus, $f_Y(y) = \dfrac{1}{3}$, $-7 \le y \le -4$.

3.7.5 $F_Y(y) = P(Y \le y) = P(2X - 3 \le y) = P\left(X \le \dfrac{1}{2}(y + 3)\right)$

$= \int_0^{\frac{1}{2}(y+3)} 6x(1-x)dx = 3x^2 - 2x^3 \Big|_0^{\frac{1}{2}(y+3)}$

$= 3\left(\dfrac{1}{2}(y+3)\right)^2 - 2\left(\dfrac{1}{2}(y+3)\right)^3 = -\dfrac{1}{4}y^3 - \dfrac{3}{2}y^2 - \dfrac{9}{4}y$

so $f_Y(y) = -\dfrac{3}{4}y^2 - 3y - \dfrac{9}{4}$, $-3 < y < -1$

3.7.7 (a) $F_Y(y) = P(Y \le y) = P(1/X \le y) = P(X \ge 1/y)$
$= 1 - P(X < 1/y) = 1 - F_X(1/y)$. Differentiating both sides of the equality gives
$f_Y(y) = \dfrac{d}{dy}(1 - F_X(1/y)) = \dfrac{1}{y^2}f_X(1/y) = \dfrac{1}{y^2}e^{-1/y},\ y > 0$

(b) $F_Y(y) = P(Y \le y) = P(\ln X \le y) = P(X \le e^y) = F_X(e^y)$. Differentiating both sides of the
equality gives $f_Y(y) = \dfrac{d}{dy}F_X(e^y) = e^y f_X(e^y) = e^y e^{-e^y},\ -\infty < y < \infty$

3.7.9 $F_Y(y) = P(Y \le y) = P(4X^2 \le y) = P\left(X \le \sqrt{y}/2\right) = F_X\left(\sqrt{y}/2\right)$

Thus, $f_Y(y) = \dfrac{1}{4\sqrt{y}} f_X\left(\sqrt{y}/2\right) = \dfrac{1}{4\sqrt{y}} 3\left(\sqrt{y}/2\right)^2 = \dfrac{3}{16}\sqrt{y}$, $0 < y < 4$

3.7.11 $F_Y(y) = P(Y \le y) =$

$P\left(\dfrac{5}{9}(X - 32) \le y\right) = P\left(X \le \dfrac{9}{5}y + 32\right) = F_X\left(\dfrac{9}{5}y + 32\right)$

Thus, $f_Y(y) = \dfrac{9}{5} f_X\left(\dfrac{9}{5}y + 32\right) = \left(\dfrac{81}{25}y + \dfrac{288}{5}\right) e^{-\left(\frac{9}{5}+32\right)^2/2}$ where $y > -160/9$.

3.7.13   First suppose that $0 < z \le 1$. $F_Z(z) = P(Z \le z) = P(X + Y \le z)$. The region of integration is the right triangle with vertices at $(0, 0)$, $(0, z)$, and $(z, 0)$. Because the density is uniform, the integration is simply equal to the area of the figure. The region of integration is a right triangle, with sides of length z. The area is then $\dfrac{1}{2}z^2$.

If $1 < z < 2$, the region of integration is the unit square minus the triangle with vertices $(1, 1)$, $(z - 1, 1)$ and $(1, z - 1)$. The triangle is a right triangle with sides of length $2 - z$. Thus, the area of the region of integration is $1 - \dfrac{1}{2}(2 - z)^2$.

In summary then

$$F_Z(z) = \begin{cases} \dfrac{1}{2}z^2 & 0 < z \le 1 \\[2mm] 1 - \dfrac{1}{2}(2 - z)^2 & 1 < z < 2 \end{cases}$$

3.7.15 $F_Z(z) = P(X/Y \le z) = P(Y \ge (1/z)X)$.

First, suppose, $0 < z \le 1$. The region of integration is a triangle with vertices $(0, 0)$, $(0, 1)$, and $(z, 1)$. Since the joint density is uniform, $F_Z(z)$ is the area of the figure. The region of integration is a right triangle with sides 1 and z, which is $\dfrac{1}{2}z$.

If $1 < z$, the region of integration is the unit square with a right triangle of sides 1 and $1/z$ removed. Thus, the area is $1 - \dfrac{1}{2z}$. In summary,

$$F_Z(z) = \begin{cases} \dfrac{1}{2}z & 0 < z \le 1 \\[2mm] 1 - \dfrac{1}{2z} & 1 < z \end{cases}$$

The pdf is obtained by integrating each branch of the rule:

$$f_Z(z) = \begin{cases} \dfrac{1}{2} & 0 < z \le 1 \\[2mm] \dfrac{1}{2z^2} & 1 < z \end{cases}$$

3.7.17 From Example 3.7.6, we know that

$$P(Z=z) = \sum_{k=0}^{z} P(X=k)P(Y=z-k) = \sum_{k=0}^{z} \frac{e^{-r}r^k}{k!} \frac{e^{-s}s^{z-k}}{(z-k)!}$$

$$= \frac{e^{-(r+s)}}{z!} \sum_{k=0}^{z} \frac{z!}{k!(z-k)!} r^k s^{z-k}$$

The summation is a binomial sum and equals $(r+s)^z$. Thus, $P(Z=z) = \dfrac{e^{-(r+s)}}{z!}(r+s)^z$. We recognize this density as Poisson with parameter $r+s$. The Poisson density reproduces itself under addition.

3.7.19 In a manner similar to Example 3.7.7, we have

$$F_Z(z) = \int_0^z xe^{-x}\left(\int_0^{z-x} e^{-y}dy\right)dx = \int_0^z xe^{-x}(1-e^{x-z})dx = \int_0^z (xe^{-x} - xe^{-z})dx$$

$$= -(x+1)e^{-x}\Big|_0^z - \frac{x^2}{2}e^{-z}\Big|_0^z = -(z+1)e^{-z} + 1 - \frac{z^2}{2}e^{-z}$$

Differentiating the above quantity gives

$$f_Z(z) = \frac{z^2}{2}e^{-z}, z > 0$$

3.7.21 $f_{X+Y}(z) = \int_0^\infty f_X(x)f_Y(z-x)dx = \int_0^z e^{-x}e^{-(z-x)}dx$. The upper limit on the integral changes to z, because $f_Y(z-x) = 0$ unless $z-x > 0$, or equivalently, $x < z$.

So $f_{X+Y}(z) = \int_0^z e^{-z}dx = xe^{-z}\Big|_0^z = ze^{-z}, z > 0$

3.7.23 $f_Y(y) = \frac{1}{3}f_X\left(\frac{y-(-1)}{3}\right) = \frac{1}{3}2\left(\frac{y+1}{3}\right) = \frac{2}{9}(y+1), -1 < y < 2$

3.7.25 From Example 3.7.7 or Question 3.7.21, we know that $f_{X_1+X_2}(y) = ye^{-y}, y > 0$.

Then, $f_{X_1+X_2+X_3}(z) = \int_0^z ye^{-y}e^{-(z-y)}dy = \int_0^z ye^{-z}dy = \frac{y^2}{2}e^{-z}\Big|_0^z = \frac{z^2}{2}e^{-z}$, with $z > 0$.

Section 3.8

3.8.1 $P(Y_3' < 5) = \int_0^5 f_{Y_3}(y)dy$

$$= \int_0^5 \frac{4!}{(3-1)!(4-3)!} \frac{y}{10}^{3-1}\left(1-\frac{y}{10}\right)^{4-3}\frac{1}{10}dy$$

$$= \frac{12}{10^4}\int_0^5 y^2(10-y)dy = \frac{12}{10^4}\left[\frac{10}{3}y^3 - \frac{1}{4}y^4\right]_0^5$$

$$= \frac{12}{10^4}\left[\frac{10}{3}5^3 - \frac{1}{4}5^4\right] = 5/16$$

3.8.3 $P(Y_2' > y_{60}) = 1 - P(Y_2' < y_{60}) = 1 - P(Y_1 < y_{60}, Y_2 < y_{60})$
$= 1 - P(Y_1 < y_{60})P(Y_2 < y_{60}) = 1 - (0.60)(0.60) = 0.64$

3.8.5 $P(Y_1' > m) = P(Y_1, \ldots, Y_n > m) = \left(\dfrac{1}{2}\right)^n$

$P(Y_n' > m) = 1 - P(Y_n' < m) = 1 - P(Y_1, \ldots, Y_n < m)$

$= 1 - P(Y_1 < m) \cdot \ldots \cdot P(Y_n < m) = 1 - \left(\dfrac{1}{2}\right)^n$

If $n \geq 2$, the latter probability is greater.

3.8.7 $P(0.6 < Y_4' < 0.7) = F_{Y_4'}(0.7) - F_{Y_4'}(0.6)$

$= \displaystyle\int_{0.6}^{0.7} \dfrac{6!}{(4-1)!\,(6-4)!} y^{4-1}(1-y)^{6-4}(1)dy$ (by Theorem 3.8.1)

$= \displaystyle\int_{0.6}^{0.7} 60y^3(1-y)^2\,dy = \int_{0.6}^{0.7} 60(y^3 - 2y^4 + y^5)dy$

$= 15y^4 - 24y^5 + 10y^6 \Big|_{0.6}^{0.7} = 0.74431 - 0.54432 = 0.19999$

3.8.9 $P(Y_{\min} > 20) = P(Y_1 > 20, Y_2 > 20, \ldots, Y_n > 20) = P(Y_1 > 20)P(Y_2 > 20) \ldots P(Y_n > 20)$
$= [P(Y > 20)]^n$. But 20 is the median of Y, so $P(Y > 20) = 1/2$. Thus, $P(Y_{\min} > 20) = (1/2)^n$.

3.8.11 The graphed pdf is the function $f_Y(y) = 2y$, so $f_Y(y) = y^2$
Then $f_{Y_4'}(y) = 20y^6(1-y^2)2y = 40y^7(1-y^2)$ and $F_{Y_4'}(y) = 5y^8 - 4y^{10}$.

$P(Y_4' > 0.75) = 1 - F_{Y_4'}(0.75) = 1 - 0.275 = 0.725$

The probability that none of the schools will have fewer than 10% of their students bused is

$P(Y_{\min} > 0.1) = 1 - F_{Y_{\min}}(0.1) = 1 - \displaystyle\int_0^{0.1} 10y(1-y^2)^4\,dy$

$= 1 - \left[-(1-y^2)^5 \right]_0^{0.1} = 0.951$ (see Question 3.8.8)

Section 3.9

3.9.1 $P(X = 2 \mid Y = 2) = \dfrac{P(X = 2, Y = 2)}{P(Y = 2)}$

$= \dfrac{\dbinom{4}{2}\dbinom{4}{2}\dbinom{44}{1}}{\dbinom{52}{5}} \div \dfrac{\dbinom{4}{2}\dbinom{48}{3}}{\dbinom{52}{5}} = \dfrac{\dbinom{4}{2}\dbinom{4}{2}\dbinom{44}{1}}{\dbinom{4}{2}\dbinom{48}{3}} = 0.015$

3.9.3 $\quad p_{Y|x}(y) = \dfrac{p_{X,Y}(x,y)}{p_X(x)} = \dfrac{\dbinom{8}{x}\dbinom{6}{y}\dbinom{4}{3-x-y}}{\dbinom{18}{3}} \div \dfrac{\dbinom{8}{x}\dbinom{10}{3-x}}{\dbinom{18}{3}} = \dfrac{\dbinom{6}{y}\dbinom{4}{3-x-y}}{\dbinom{10}{3-x}}$, with $0 \le y \le 3-x$

3.9.5 $\quad P_Z(1) = \dfrac{(1)(1)+(2)(2)}{9(1)} = \dfrac{5}{9}$

$\qquad p_Z(2) = \dfrac{(2)(1)+(1)(2)+(2)(2)}{9(2)} = \dfrac{8}{18} = \dfrac{4}{9}$

$\qquad f_{X,Y|1}(x,y) = \dfrac{xy}{5}, \ (x,y) = (1,1),(2,2)$

$\qquad f_{X,Y|2}(x,y) = \dfrac{xy}{8}, \ (x,y) = (1,2),(2,1),(2,2)$

3.9.7 $\quad$ The pdf $p_Z(z)$ is binomial with parameters $2n$ and p, by Example 3.7.6. Also,

$$p_{X,Z}(x,z) = \binom{n}{x}p^x(1-p)^{n-x}\binom{n}{z-x}p^{z-x}(1-p)^{n-(z-x)} = \binom{n}{x}\binom{n}{z-x}p^z(1-p)^{2n-z}$$

$\qquad$ Then $p_{X|z}(z) = \dfrac{\dbinom{n}{x}\dbinom{n}{z-x}p^z(1-p)^{2n-z}}{\dbinom{2n}{z}p^z(1-p)^{2n-z}} = \dfrac{\dbinom{n}{x}\dbinom{n}{z-x}}{\dbinom{2n}{z}}$

$\qquad$ which is a hypergeometric pdf.

3.9.9 $\quad$ (a) $\ f_X(x) = \displaystyle\int_x^\infty 2e^{-x}e^{-y}dy = 2e^{-2x}, \ x > 0$

$\qquad\qquad$ So, $P(X < 1) = \displaystyle\int_0^1 2e^{-2x}dx = 1 - e^{-2} = 1 - 0.135 = 0.865$

$\qquad\qquad$ Also, $P(X < 1, Y < 1) = \displaystyle\int_0^1\int_0^x 2e^{-(x+y)}dydx$

$\qquad\qquad = \displaystyle\int_0^1 2e^{-x}\left[-e^{-y}\right]_0^x dx = \int_0^1(2e^{-x} - 2e^{-2x})dx$

$\qquad\qquad = -2e^{-x} + e^{-2x}\Big|_0^1 = 0.400$

$\qquad\qquad$ Then the conditional probability is $\dfrac{0.400}{0.865} = 0.462$

$\qquad$ (b) $\ P(Y < 1 \,|\, X = 1) = 0$, since the joint pdf is defined with y always larger than x.

$\qquad$ (c) $\ f_{Y|x}(y) = \dfrac{f_{X,Y}(x,y)}{f_X(x)} = \dfrac{2e^{-(x+y)}}{2e^{-2x}} = e^x e^{-y}, x < y$

3.9.11 $f_X(x) = \int_0^{1-x} 2\,dy = 2y\ \Big|_0^{1-x} = 2(1-x),\ 0 < x < 1$

$f_{Y|x}(y) = \dfrac{f_{X,Y}(x,y)}{f_X(x)} = \dfrac{2}{2(1-x)} = \dfrac{1}{1-x},\ 0 < y < 1-x$

For each x, the conditional pdf does not depend on y, so it is a uniform pdf.

3.9.13 (a) $f_X(x) = \int_0^1 \dfrac{2}{5}(2x+3y)dy = \dfrac{2}{5}\left(2xy + \dfrac{3}{2}y^2\right)\Big|_0^1 = \dfrac{4}{5}x + \dfrac{3}{5}$, with $0 < x < 1$

(b) $f_{Y|x}(y) = \dfrac{\dfrac{2}{5}(2x+3y)}{\dfrac{4}{5}x + \dfrac{3}{5}} = \dfrac{4x+6y}{4x+3},\ 0 < y < 1$

(c) $f_{Y|\frac{1}{2}}(y) = \dfrac{1}{5}(2+6y)$

$P(1/4 \le Y \le 3/4) = \int_{1/4}^{3/4} \dfrac{1}{5}(2+6y)dy = 10/20 = 1/2$

3.9.15 $f_Y(y) = \int_0^y \dfrac{xy}{2}dx = \dfrac{x^2y}{4}\Big|_0^y = \dfrac{y^3}{4},\ 0 < y < 2$

$f_{X|y}(x) = \dfrac{xy}{2}\Big/\dfrac{y^3}{4} = \dfrac{2x}{y^2},\ 0 < x < y$

$f_{X|\frac{3}{2}}(x) = \dfrac{2x}{(3/2)^2} = \dfrac{8}{9}x,\ 0 < x < 3/2$

$P(X < 1 \mid Y = 3/2) = \int_0^1 \dfrac{8}{9}x\,dx = \dfrac{4}{9}x^2\Big|_0^1 = \dfrac{4}{9}$

3.9.17 (a) $f_X(x) = \int_0^2 \dfrac{6}{7}\left(x^2 + \dfrac{xy}{2}\right)dy = \dfrac{6}{7}\left(x^2y + \dfrac{xy^2}{4}\right)\Big|_0^2 = \dfrac{6}{7}(2x^2 + x)$

(b) $P(X > 2Y) = \int_0^1 \int_0^{\frac{1}{2}x} \dfrac{6}{7}\left(x^2 + \dfrac{xy}{2}\right)dydx$

$= \int_0^1 \left[\dfrac{6}{7}\left(x^2y + \dfrac{xy^2}{4}\right)\right]_0^{\frac{1}{2}x} dx = \int_0^1 \dfrac{6}{7}\left(\dfrac{9}{16}x^3\right)dx = \dfrac{27}{224}$

(c) $P(X > 1/2,\, Y > 1) = \dfrac{P(X > 1/2,\, Y > 1)}{P(X > 1/2)}$

First calculate the numerator:

$P(X > 1/2,\, Y > 1) = \int_{1/2}^1 \int_1^2 \dfrac{6}{7}\left(x^2 + \dfrac{xy}{2}\right)dydx = \dfrac{55}{112}$

We know f_X from part (a) so the denominator is

$$P(X > 1/2) = \int_{1/2}^{1} \frac{6}{7}(2x^2 + x)dx = \frac{23}{28}$$

The conditional probability requested is $\dfrac{55}{112} \Big/ \dfrac{23}{28} = \dfrac{55}{92}$

Section 3.10

3.10.1 $E(X) = -1(0.935) + 2(0.0514) + 18(0.0115) + 180(0.0016) + 1{,}300(1.35 \times 10^{-4})$
$+ 2{,}600(6.12 \times 10^{-6}) + 10{,}000(1.12 \times 10^{-7}) = -0.144668$

3.10.3 Rule A:

$$\text{Expected value} = -5 + 0 \cdot \frac{\binom{2}{0}\binom{4}{2}}{\binom{6}{2}} + 2 \cdot \frac{\binom{2}{1}\binom{4}{1}}{\binom{6}{2}} + 10 \cdot \frac{\binom{2}{2}\binom{4}{0}}{\binom{6}{2}} = -49/15$$

Rule B:

$$\text{Expected value} = -5 + 0 \cdot \frac{\binom{2}{0}\binom{4}{2}}{\binom{6}{2}} + 1 \cdot \frac{\binom{2}{1}\binom{4}{1}}{\binom{6}{2}} + 20 \cdot \frac{\binom{2}{2}\binom{4}{0}}{\binom{6}{2}} = -47/15$$

Neither game is fair to the player, but Rule B has the better payoff.

3.10.5 The number of minorities is a hypergeometric random variable with $r = 575$, $w = 3015$, and $n = 250$. Then $E(X) = \dfrac{rn}{r+w} = \dfrac{575(250)}{575+3015} = 40.0$

3.10.7 (a) $E(Y) = \int_0^1 y \cdot 3(1-y)^2\,dy = \int_0^1 3(y - 2y^2 + y^3)\,dy$

$$= 3\left[\frac{1}{2}y^2 - \frac{2}{3}y^3 + \frac{1}{4}y^4\right]_0^1 = \frac{1}{4}$$

(b) $E(Y) = \int_0^\infty y \cdot 4ye^{-2y}\,dy = 4\left[-\frac{1}{2}y^2 e^{-2y} - \frac{1}{2}ye^{-2y} - \frac{1}{4}e^{-2y}\right]_0^\infty = e^{-2y}$

(c) $E(Y) = \int_0^1 y \cdot \left(\frac{3}{4}\right)dy + \int_2^3 y \cdot \left(\frac{1}{4}\right)dy = \frac{3y^2}{8}\Big|_0^1 + \frac{y^2}{8}\Big|_2^3 = 1$

(d) $E(Y) = \int_0^{\pi/2} y \cdot \sin y\,dy = -y\cos y + \sin y\,\Big|_0^{\pi/2} = 1$

3.10.9 $E(Y) = \int_a^b y \frac{1}{b-a} dy = \frac{y^2}{2(b-a)} \Big|_a^b = \frac{b^2}{2(b-a)} - \frac{a^2}{2(b-a)} = \frac{b+a}{2}$. This simply says that a uniform bar will balance at its middle.

3.10.11 Let X be the number of cars passing the emissions test. Then X is binomial with $n = 200$ and $p = 0.80$. Two formulas for $E(X)$ are:

(1) $E(X) = \sum_{k=1}^{n} k \binom{n}{k} p^k (1-p)^{n-k} = \sum_{k=1}^{200} k \binom{200}{k} 0.80^k 0.20^{200-k}$

(2) $E(X) = np = 200(0.80) = 160$

3.10.13 If birthdays are randomly distributed throughout the year, the city should expect revenue of ($50)(74,806)(30/365) or $307,421.92.

3.10.15 From the quotation of 18 words is derived the following frequency table:

Word length, k	No. of occurences	Estimated $p_X(k)$
1	1	1/18
2	4	4/18
3	7	7/18
4	4	4/18
5	0	0
6	1	1/18
7	1	1/18

Then $E(X) = 1(1/18) + 2(4/18) + 3(7/18) + 4(4/18) + 5(0) + 6(1/18) + 7(1/18) = 59/18$

3.10.17 The probability that the head appears on the k-th toss is $(1/2)^k$, $k = 1, 2, \ldots$. The k-th payoff is that same value.

$$E(X) = \sum_{k=1}^{\infty} \left(\frac{1}{2}\right)^k \left(\frac{1}{2}\right)^k = \sum_{k=1}^{\infty} \left(\frac{1}{4}\right)^k = \frac{1}{4} \sum_{k=0}^{\infty} \left(\frac{1}{4}\right)^k = \frac{1}{4} \frac{1}{1-\frac{1}{4}} = \frac{1}{3}$$

3.10.19 (a) $E(X) = \sum_{k=1}^{\infty} c^k \left(\frac{1}{2}\right)^k = \sum_{k=1}^{\infty} \left(\frac{c}{2}\right)^k = \frac{c}{2} \sum_{k=0}^{\infty} \left(\frac{c}{2}\right)^k = \frac{c}{2-c}$

(b) $\sum_{k=1}^{\infty} \log 2^k \left(\frac{1}{2}\right)^k = \log 2 \sum_{k=1}^{\infty} k \left(\frac{1}{2}\right)^k$.

To evaluate the sum requires a special technique: For a parameter t, $0 < t < 1$, note that

$\sum_{k=1}^{\infty} t^k = \frac{t}{1-t}$. Differentiate both sides of the equation with respect to t to obtain

$\sum_{k=1}^{\infty} k t^{k-1} = \frac{1}{(1-t)^2}$. Multiplying both sides by t gives the desired equation:

$\sum_{k=1}^{\infty} k t^k = \frac{t}{(1-t)^2}$. In the case of interest, $t = 1/2$, so $\sum_{k=1}^{\infty} k \left(\frac{1}{2}\right)^k = 2$,

and $E(X) = 2 \cdot \log 2$.

3.10.21 For the experiment described, construct the table

Sample	Absolute value of difference
1, 2	1
1, 3	2
1, 4	3
1, 5	4
2, 3	1
2, 4	2
2, 5	3
3, 4	1
3, 5	2
4, 5	1

If X denotes the absolute value of difference, then from the table,
$$p_X(1) = 4/10,\ p_X(2) = 3/10,\ p_X(3) = 2/10,\ p_X(4) = 1/10$$
$$E(X) = 1(4/10) + 2(3/10) + 3(2/10) + 4(1/10) = 2$$

3.10.23 Let X = number of drawings to obtain a white chip. Then

$$p_X(k) = \frac{1}{k} \cdot \frac{1}{k+1},\ k = 1,\ 2,\ \ldots$$

$$E(X) = \sum_{k=1}^{\infty} k \left(\frac{1}{k(k+1)} \right) = \sum_{k=1}^{\infty} \frac{1}{k+1}.$$

For each n, let $T_n = \sum_{i=2^n}^{i=2^{n+1}} \frac{1}{i}$. Then $T_n \geq \frac{2^n}{2^{n+1}} = \frac{1}{2}$.

$$\sum_{k=1}^{\infty} \frac{1}{k+1} \geq \sum_{n=1}^{\infty} T_n = \frac{1}{2} + \frac{1}{2} + \frac{1}{2} + \cdots \quad \text{This last sum is infinite, so } E(X) \text{ does not exist.}$$

3.10.25 $E(X) = \displaystyle\sum_{j=1}^{\infty} j f_X(j) = \sum_{j=1}^{\infty} \sum_{k=1}^{j} f_X(j) = \sum_{k=1}^{\infty} \sum_{j=k}^{\infty} f_X(j) = \sum_{k=1}^{\infty} P(X \geq k)$

3.10.27 $f_X(x) = \displaystyle\int_0^1 (x + y)\,dy = xy + \frac{y^2}{2}\bigg|_0^1 = x + \frac{1}{2},\ 0 < x < 1$

$$E(Y\,|\,x) = \int_0^1 y \frac{(x + y)}{x + \dfrac{1}{2}}\,dy = \frac{1}{x + \dfrac{1}{2}} \int_0^1 (xy + y^2)\,dy$$

$$= \frac{1}{x + \dfrac{1}{2}} \left[\frac{xy^2}{2} + \frac{y^3}{3} \right]_0^1 = \frac{\dfrac{1}{2}x + \dfrac{1}{3}}{x + \dfrac{1}{2}} = \frac{3x + 2}{6x + 3}$$

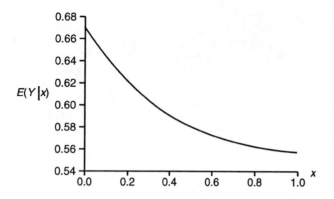

Section 3.11

3.11.1 Let X = the number of clubs among the eight cards drawn.

Then $X = \sum_{i=1}^{8} X_i$ and $E(X) = \sum_{i=1}^{8} E(X_i)$. Each X_i has $E(X_i) = 1(1/4) + 0(3/4) = 1/4$.

Thus, $E(X) = 8(1/4) = 2$.

3.11.3 Let X_i be the daily closing price of the stock on day i. The daily expected gain is $E(X_i) = (1/8)p - (1/8)q = (1/8)(p - q)$. After n days the expected gain is $(n/8)(p - q)$.

3.11.5 Let $X_i = 1$ if a shot with the first gun is a bull'e eye and 0 otherwise, $i = 1, \ldots, 10$. $E(X_i) = 0.30$. Let $V_i = 1$ if a shot with the second gun is a bull's-eye and 0 otherwise, $i = 1, \ldots, 10$. $E(V_i) = 0.40$.

Cathie's score is $4\sum_{i=1}^{10} X_i + 6\sum_{i=1}^{10} V_i$, and her expected score is $E\left(4\sum_{i=1}^{10} X_i + 6\sum_{i=1}^{10} V_i\right) =$

$4\sum_{i=1}^{10} E(X_i) + 6\sum_{i=1}^{10} E(V_i) = 4(10)(0.30) + 6(10)(0.40) = 36$.

3.11.7 (1) First find $f_Y(y)$: $F_Y(y) = P(Y \le y) = P(X^3 \le y) = P(X \le y^{1/3}) = F_X(y^{1/3})$.

Then $f_Y(y) = \frac{1}{3}y^{-2/3}f_X(y^{1/3}) = \frac{2}{3}(y^{-2/3} - y^{-1/3})$

$E(Y) = \int_0^1 y\frac{2}{3}(y^{-2/3} - y^{-1/3}) = \frac{2}{3}\int_0^1 (y^{1/3} - y^{2/3})dy$

$= \frac{2}{3}\left[\left(\frac{3}{4}y^{4/3} - \frac{3}{5}y^{5/3}\right)\right]_0^1 = \frac{1}{10}$

(2) $E(Y) = \int_0^1 x^2 2(1-x)dx = 2\int_0^1 (x^3 - x^4)dx$

$= 2\left[\frac{x^4}{4} - \frac{x^5}{5}\right]_0^1 = \frac{1}{10}$

3.11.9 $E(\text{Volume}) = \int_0^\infty 5y^2 6y(1-y)dy = 30\int_0^1(y^3 - y^4)dy = 30\left[\dfrac{1}{4}y^4 - \dfrac{1}{5}y^5\right]_0^1 = 1.5 \text{ in}^3$

3.11.11 For the graph pictured to be a pdf, $t = 4$ and $f_Y(y) = y/8$.

$$E(Y^2) = \int_0^4 y^2 \frac{y}{8}dy = \frac{1}{8}\int_0^4 y^3 dy = \frac{y^4}{32}\bigg|_0^4 = 8$$

3.11.13 $1 = \displaystyle\sum_{i=1}^n ki = k\dfrac{n(n+1)}{2}$ implies $k = \dfrac{2}{n(n+1)}$

$E\left(\dfrac{1}{X}\right) = \displaystyle\sum_{i=1}^n \dfrac{1}{i}\dfrac{2}{n(n+1)}i = 2/(n+1)$

3.11.15 $E(X+Y) = \displaystyle\int_0^\infty \int_0^\infty (x+y)e^{-x-y}dydx = \int_0^\infty e^{-x}\int_0^\infty (x+y)e^{-y}dydx$

$= \displaystyle\int_0^\infty e^{-x}\left[-xe^{-y} - (y+1)e^{-y}\right]_0^\infty dx = \int_0^\infty (x+1)e^{-x}dx = 2$

3.11.17 $E(\text{Area}) = \displaystyle\int_0^1 \int_0^1 xy \cdot 1 \, dydx = 1/4$

3.11.19 Let X_1 = number showing on face 1; X_2 = number showing on face 2. Since X_1 and X_2 are independent, $E(X_1 X_2) = E(X_1)E(X_2) = (3.5)(3.5) = 12.25$.

Section 3.12

3.12.1 If sampling is done with replacement, X is binomial with $n = 2$ and $p = 2/5$. By Example, 3.10.5, $\mu = 2(2/5) = 4/5$.
$E(X^2) = 0 \cdot (9/25) + 1 \cdot (12/25) + 4 \cdot (4/25) = 28/25$. Then $\text{Var}(X) = 28/25 - (4/5)^2 = 12/25$.

3.12.3 Since X is hypergeometric, $\mu = \dfrac{3(6)}{10} = \dfrac{9}{5}$

$$E(X^2) = \sum_{k=0}^3 k^2 \frac{\binom{6}{k}\binom{4}{3-k}}{\binom{10}{3}} = 0 \cdot (4/120) + 1 \cdot (36/120) + 4 \cdot (60/12) + 9 \cdot (20/120) =$$

$456/120 = 38/10$
$\text{Var}(X) = 38/10 - (9/5)^2 = 28/50 = 0.56$, and $\sigma = 0.748$.

3.12.5 $\mu = \displaystyle\int_0^1 y3(1-y)^2 dy = 3\int_0^1(y - 2y^2 + y^3)dy = 1/4$

$E(Y^2) = \displaystyle\int_0^1 y^2 3(1-y)^2 dy = 3\int_0^1(y^2 - 2y^3 + y^4)dy = 1/10$

$\text{Var}(Y) = 1/10 - (1/4)^2 = 3/80$

3.12.7 $f_Y(y) = \begin{cases} 1-y, & 0 \le y \le 1 \\ 1/2, & 2 \le y \le 3 \\ 0, & \text{elsewhere} \end{cases}$

$$\mu = \int_0^1 y(1-y)dy + \int_2^3 y\left(\frac{1}{2}\right)dy = 17/12$$

$$E(Y^2) = \int_0^1 y^2(1-y)dy + \int_2^3 y^2\left(\frac{1}{2}\right)dy = 13/4$$

$$\sigma = \sqrt{13/4 - (17/12)^2} = \sqrt{179}/12 = 1.115$$

3.12.9 Let $Y =$ Frankie's selection. Johnny wants to choose k so that $E[(Y-k)^2]$ is minimized. The minimum occurs when $k = E(Y) = (a+b)/2$ (see Question 3.12.11).

3.12.11 $E[(X-a)^2] = E[((X-\mu) + (\mu-a))^2]$
$= E[(X-\mu)^2] + E[(\mu-a)^2] + 2(\mu-a)E(X-\mu)$
$= \text{Var}(X) + (\mu-a)^2$, since $E(X-\mu) = 0$. This is minimized when $a = \mu$, so the minimum of $g(a) = \text{Var}(X)$.

Section 3.13

3.13.1 (1) $E[W-\mu)/\sigma] = (1/\sigma)E[(W-\mu)] = 0$
(2) $\text{Var}[(W-\mu)/\sigma] = (1/\sigma^2)\text{Var}[(W-\mu)] = (1/\sigma^2)\sigma^2 = 1$

3.13.3 Let $X = (Y - 2000)/1000$. Then X is uniform over the interval $(-1, 1)$.

$$\text{Var}(X) = \int_{-1}^1 (x-0)^2 \left(\frac{1}{2}\right)dx = \left.\frac{x^3}{6}\right|_{-1}^1 = 1/3.$$

Also, $\text{Var}(X) = \text{Var}((Y-2000)/1000) = \text{Var}(Y)/1000^2$, so
$\text{Var}(Y) = (1,000,000)\text{Var}(X) = 1,000,000/3$

3.13.5 $E(W) = E(4X + 6Y) = 4E(X) + 6E(Y) = 4np_X + 6mp_Y$
$\text{Var}(W) = \text{Var}(4X + 6Y) = 16\text{Var}(X) + 36\text{Var}(Y) =$
$= 16np_X(1 - p_X) + 36mp_Y(1 - p_Y)$

3.13.7 The proof of Theorem 3.13.2 demonstrated the case $n = 2$. Now suppose the theorem is true for $n - 1$. $\text{Var}(W_1 + W_2 + \ldots W_n) = \text{Var}[(W_1 + W_2 + \ldots W_{n-1}) + W_n] = \text{Var}(W_1 + W_2 + \ldots + W_{n-1}) + \text{Var}(W_n)$ by the proof of the theorem. By the induciton hypothesis, $\text{Var}(W_1 + W_2 + \ldots W_{n-1}) = \text{Var}(W_1) + \text{Var}(W_2) + \ldots + \text{Var}(W_{n-1})$. Thus, $\text{Var}(W_1 + W_2 + \ldots W_n) = \text{Var}(W_1) + \text{Var}(W_2) + \ldots + \text{Var}(W_{n-1}) + \text{Var}(W_n)$, which was to be shown.

3.13.9 $\text{Var}\left(\frac{2D}{T^2}\right) = 4\text{Var}\left(\frac{D}{T^2}\right) = 4\left(\frac{1}{\mu_T^2}\right)^2 \sigma_D^2 + 4\left(\frac{-2\mu_D}{\mu_T^3}\right)\sigma_T^2$

$= \frac{4}{\mu_T^4}\left(\sigma_D^2 + \frac{4\mu_D^2}{\mu_T^2}\sigma_T^2\right) = \frac{4}{\mu_T^4}\left((0.0025)^2 + \frac{4\mu_D^2}{\mu_T^2}(0.045)^2\right)$

For the first set up, this last expression becomes

$$\frac{4}{(0.5)^4}\left((0.0025)^2 + \frac{4(4^2)}{(0.5)^2}(0.045)^2\right) = 33.178$$

For the second set up, the approximation is

$$\frac{4}{(1)^4}\left((0.0025)^2 + \frac{4(16^2)}{(1)^2}(0.045)^2\right) = 8.294$$

3.13.11 $\sigma_A^2 = \left(\frac{1}{2}\mu_h\right)^2(\sigma_a^2 + \sigma_b^2) + \left[\frac{1}{2}(\mu_a + \mu_b)\right]^2\sigma_h^2$, so

$$\sigma_A = \frac{1}{2}\sqrt{\mu_h^2\sigma_a^2 + \mu_h^2\sigma_b^2 + (\mu_a + \mu_b)^2\sigma_h^2}$$

Section 3.14

3.14.1 (a) Since $E(Y) = \text{Var}(Y) = 1$, we seek $P(|Y - 1| > 2) = P(Y > 3) = e^{-3} = 0.050$

(b) By Chebyshev's inequality, $P(|Y - 1| > 2) \le \dfrac{\text{Var}(Y)}{2^2} = \dfrac{1}{4} = 0.25$

3.14.3 $P(Y \le 52 \text{ or } Y \ge 148) = P(|Y - 100| \ge 48) \le \dfrac{16^2}{48^2} = \dfrac{1}{9}$

Section 3.15

3.15.1 $E(Y^r) = \displaystyle\int_0^2 y^r \frac{1}{2}\,dy = \frac{1}{2}\frac{y^{r+1}}{r+1}\bigg|_0^2 = \frac{2^r}{r+1}$

$$E[(Y-1)^6] = \sum_{j=0}^6 \binom{6}{j}E(Y^j)(-1)^{6-j} = \sum_{j=0}^6 \binom{6}{j}\frac{2^r}{r+1}(-1)^{6-j}$$

$$= (1)(1) + (-6)(1) + 15(4/3) + (-20)(2) + (15)(16/5) + (-6)(32/6) + (1)(64/7) = 1/7$$

3.15.3 $10 = E[(W-2)^3] = \displaystyle\sum_{j=0}^3 \binom{3}{j}E(W^j)(-2)^{3-j}$

$$= (1)(1)(-8) + (3)(2)(4) + (3)E(W^2)(-2) + (1)(4)(1)$$
This would imply that $E(W^2) = 5/3$, which is possible.

3.15.5 (a) $1 = \int_1^\infty cy^{-6}dy = c\left[\dfrac{y^{-5}}{-5}\right]_1^\infty = c\dfrac{1}{5}$, so $c = 5$.

(b) $E(Y^r) = 5\int_1^\infty y^r y^{-6}dy = 5\left[\dfrac{y^{r-5}}{r-5}\right]_1^\infty$ For this last expression to be finite, r must be < 5.

The highest integral moment is $r = 4$.

Section 3.16

3.16.1 $M_X(t) = \displaystyle\sum_{k=1}^\infty e^{tk}p(1-p)^{k-1} = pe^t\sum_{k=1}^\infty e^{t(k-1)}(1-p)^{k-1}$

$= pe^t\displaystyle\sum_{k=0}^\infty e^{tk}(1-p)^k = pe^t\dfrac{1}{1-e^t(1-p)}$

$= pe^t\dfrac{1}{1-qe^t}$, $0 < qe^t < 1$

3.16.3 For the given binomial random variable,

$E(e^{tX}) = M_X(t) = \left(1 - \dfrac{1}{3} + \dfrac{1}{3}e^t\right)^{10}$. Set $t = 3$ to obtain $E(e^{3X}) = \dfrac{1}{3^{10}}(2+e^3)^{10}$

3.16.5 $M_X(t) = \displaystyle\int_{-1}^2 e^{tx}\dfrac{1}{3}\,dx = \dfrac{1}{3t}e^{tx}\Big|_{-1}^2 = \dfrac{1}{3t}(e^{2t} - e^{-t})$ for $t \neq 0$.

$M_X(0) = \displaystyle\lim_{t\to 0}\dfrac{1}{3t}(e^{2t}-e^{-t}) = \lim_{t\to 0}\dfrac{\dfrac{d}{dt}(e^{2t}-e^{-t})}{\dfrac{d}{dt}3t}$ by

L'Hospital's rule. Thus, $M_X(0) = \displaystyle\lim_{t\to 0}\dfrac{(2e^{2t}+e^{-t})}{3} = 1$

3.16.7 $M_X(t) = E(e^{tX}) = \displaystyle\sum_{k=0}^\infty e^{tk}e^{-\lambda}\dfrac{\lambda^k}{k!} = e^{-\lambda}\sum_{k=0}^\infty \dfrac{(\lambda e^t)^k}{k!} = e^{\lambda(e^t-1)}$

3.16.9 $M_X^{(1)}(t) = \dfrac{d}{dt}e^{-\lambda+\lambda e^t} = \lambda e^t e^{-\lambda+\lambda e^t}$, so $E(X) = M_X^{(1)}(0) = \lambda$

$M_X^{(2)}(t) = (\lambda e^t)^2 e^{-\lambda+\lambda e^t} + \lambda e^t e^{-\lambda+\lambda e^t}$, so $E(X^2) = M_X^{(2)}(0) = \lambda^2 + \lambda$
Then $\text{Var}(X) = E(X^2) - E^2(X) = (\lambda^2 + \lambda) - \lambda^2 = \lambda$

3.6.11 $M_Y^{(1)}(t) = \dfrac{d}{dt}e^{at+b^2t^2/2} = (a+b^2t)e^{at+b^2t^2/2}$, so $M_Y^{(1)}(0) = a$

$M_Y^{(2)}(t) = (a+b^2t)^2 e^{at+b^2t^2/2} + b^2 e^{at+b^2t^2/2}$, so
$M_Y^{(2)}(0) = a^2 + b^2$. Then $\text{Var}(Y) = (a^2 + b^2) - a^2 = b^2$

3.16.13 The moment generating function of Y is that of a normal variable with mean $\mu = -1$ and variance $\sigma^2 = 8$. Then $E(Y^2) = \text{Var}(Y) + \mu^2 = 8 + 1 = 9$.

3.16.15 $M_Y^{(1)}(t) = \dfrac{(1-t^2)2e^{2t} - (-2t)e^{2t}}{(1-t^2)^2} = 2\dfrac{(1+t-t^2)e^{2t}}{(1-t^2)^2}$, so $E(Y) = M_Y^{(1)}(0) = 2$.

$$M_Y^{(2)}(t) = \frac{2(1-t^2)^2[(1-2t)e^{2t} + 2(1+t-t^2)e^{2t}] - 2(1-t^2)(-2t)2(1+t-t^2)e^{2t}}{(1-t^2)^4}$$

so $M_Y^{(2)}(0) = 6$. Thus $\text{Var}(Y) = E(Y^2) - \mu^2 = 6 - 4 = 2$.

3.16.17 From the moment-generating function of X, we know that it is binomial with $n = 5$ and $p = 3/4$. Then $P(X \le 2) = (1/4)^5 + 5(3/4)(1/4)^4 + 10(3/4)^2(1/4)^3 = 0.104$

3.16.19 From the moment-generating function of W, we know that $W = X + Y$, where X is Poisson with parameter 3, and Y is binomial with parameters $n = 4$ and $p = 1/3$. Also, X and Y are independent. Then
$P(W \le 1) = p_X(0)p_Y(0) + P_X(0)P_Y(1) + p_X(1)p_Y(0) = (e^{-3})(2/3)^4 + (e^{-3})4(1/3)(2/3)^3 + (3e^{-3})(2/3)^4$
$= 0.059$

3.16.21 (a) $M_W(t) = M_{3Y}(t) = M_Y(3t) = e^{\mu(3t)+\sigma^2(3t)^2/2} = e^{(3\mu)t+9\sigma^2t^2/2}$.
This last term is the moment-generating function of a normal random variable with mean 3μ and variance $9\sigma^2$, which is then the distribution of W.

(b) $M_W(t) = M_{3Y+1}(t) = e^t M_Y(3t) = e^t e^{\mu(3t)+\sigma^2(3t)^2/2} = e^{(3\mu+1)t+9\sigma^2t^2/2}$. This last term is the moment-generating function of a normal random variable with mean $3\mu + 1$ and variance $9\sigma^2$, which is then the distribution of W.

Chapter 4

Section 4.2

4.2.1 $p = P(\text{word is misspelled}) = \dfrac{1}{3250}$; $n = 6000$. Let $x = $ number of words misspelled. Using the exact binomial analysis, $P(X=0) = \dbinom{6000}{0}\left(\dfrac{1}{3250}\right)^0\left(\dfrac{3249}{3250}\right)^{6000} = 0.158$. For the Poisson approximation, $\lambda = 6000\left(\dfrac{1}{3250}\right) = 1.846$, so $P(X=0) \doteq \dfrac{e^{-1.846}(1.846)^0}{0!} = 0.158$. The agreement is not surprising because n is so large and p is so small (recall Example 4.2.1).

4.2.3 Let $X = $ number born on Poisson's birthday. Since $n = 500, p = \dfrac{1}{365}$, and $\lambda = 500 \cdot \dfrac{1}{365} = 1.370$, $P(X \le 1) = P(X=0) + P(X=1) \doteq \dfrac{e^{-1.370}(1.370)^0}{0!} + \dfrac{e^{-1.370}(1.370)^1}{1!} = 0.602$.

4.2.5 Let $X = $ number of items requiring a price check. If $p = P(\text{item requires price check}) = 0.01$ and $n = 10$, a binomial analysis gives $P(X \ge 1) = 1 - P(X=0) = 1 - \dbinom{10}{0}(0.01)^0(0.99)^{10} = 0.10$. Using the Poisson approximation, $\lambda = 10(0.01) = 0.1$ and $P(X \ge 1) = 1 - P(X=0) \doteq 1 - \dfrac{e^{-0.1}(0.1)^0}{0!} = 0.10$. The exact model that applies here is the hypergeometric, rather than the binomial, because p is a function of the previous items purchased. However, the variation in p will be essentially zero for the 10 items purchased, so the binomial and hypergeometric models in this case will be effectively the same.

4.2.7 Let $X = $ number of pieces of luggage lost. Given that $n = 120, p = \dfrac{1}{200}$, (so $\lambda = 120 \cdot \dfrac{1}{200} = 0.6$), $= P(X \ge 2) = 1 - P(X \le 1) = 1 - \displaystyle\sum_{k=0}^{1} \dfrac{e^{-0.6}(0.6)^k}{k!} = 0.122$.

4.2.9 Let $X = $ number of solar systems with intelligent life and let $p = P(\text{solar system is inhabited})$. For $n = 100,000,000,000$, $P(X \ge 1) = 1 - P(X=0) = 1 - \dbinom{1,000,000,000}{0}p^0 \cdot (1-p)^{100,000,000,000}$. Solving $1 - (1-p)^{1,000,000,000} = 0.50$ gives $p = 6.9 \times 10^{-12}$. Alternatively, it must be true that $1 - \dfrac{e^{-\lambda}\lambda^0}{0!} = 0.50$, which implies that $\lambda = -\ln(0.50) = 0.69$. But $0.69 = np = 1 \times 10^{11} \cdot p$, so $p = 6.9 \times 10^{-12}$.

4.2.11 The observed number of major changes $= 0.44$ $(= \bar{x} = \dfrac{1}{356}[237(0) + 90(1) + 22(2) + 7(3)])$,

so the presumed Poisson model is $p_X(k) = \dfrac{e^{-0.44}(0.44)^k}{k!}$, $k = 0, 1, \ldots$ Judging from the
agreement evident in the accompanying table between the set of observed proportions and the
values for $p_X(k)$, the hypothesis that X is a Poisson random variable is entirely credible.

No. of changes, k	Frequency	Proportion	$p_X(k)$
0	237	0.666	0.6440
1	90	0.253	0.2834
2	22	0.062	0.0623
3+	7	0.020	0.0102
	356	1.00	1.00

4.2.13 a) The model $p_X(k) = e^{-2.157}(2.157)^k/k!$, $k = 0, 1, \ldots$ fits the data fairly well (where $\bar{x} = 2.157$), but there does appear to be a slight tendency for deaths to "cluster"— that is, the values 0, 5, 6, 7, 8, and 9 are all over-represented.

No. of deaths, k	Frequency	$p_X(k)$	Expected frequency
0	162	0.1157	126.8
1	267	0.2495	273.5
2	271	0.2691	294.9
3	185	0.1935	212.1
4	111	0.1043	114.3
5	61	0.0450	49.3
6	27	0.0162	17.8
7	8	0.0050	5.5
8	3	0.0013	1.4
9	1	0.0003	0.3
10+	0	0.0001	0.1

b) Deaths may not be independent events in all cases, and the fatality rate may not be constant.

4.2.15 Let $X =$ number of repairs needed during an eight-hour workday. Since $E(X) = \lambda = 8 \cdot \dfrac{1}{5} =$
1.6, $P(\text{expenses} \leq \$100) = P(X \leq 2) = \displaystyle\sum_{k=0}^{2} \dfrac{e^{-1.6}(1.6)^k}{k!} = 0.783$.

4.2.17 If $P(X = 0) = e^{-\lambda}\lambda^0/0! = e^{-\lambda} = \dfrac{1}{3}$, then $\lambda = 1.10$. Therefore, $P(X \geq 2) = 1 - P(X \leq 1) =$
$1 - e^{-1.10}(1.10)^0/0! - e^{-1.10}(1.10)^1/1! = 0.301$.

4.2.19 Let X = number of particles counted in next two minutes. Since the rate at which the particles are counted <u>per minute</u> is $4.017 \left(= \dfrac{482}{120} \right)$, $E(X) = 8.034$ and $P(X = 3) = \dfrac{e^{-8.034}(8.034)^3}{3!} = 0.028$. Now, suppose X = number of particles counted <u>in one minute</u>. Then $P(3$ particles are counted in next two minutes$) = P(X = 3) \cdot P(X = 0) + P(X = 2) \cdot P(X = 1) + P(X = 1) \cdot P(X = 2) + P(X = 0) \cdot P(X = 3) = 0.028$, where $\lambda = 4.017$.

4.2.21 If $P(X = 1) = P(X = 2)$, then $e^{-\lambda}\lambda^1/1! = e^{-\lambda}\lambda^2/2!$, which implies that $2\lambda = \lambda^2$, or, equivalently, $\lambda = 2$. Therefore, $P(X = 4) = e^{-2}2^4/4! = 0.09$.

4.2.23 $P_{X_1|x}(x_1) = P(X_1 = x_1 | X = x) = \dfrac{P(X_1 = x_1 \text{ and } X_2 = x - x_1)}{P(X = x)} = \dfrac{e^{-2}2^{x_1}/x_1! \cdot e^{-2}2^{x-x_1}/(x - x_1)!}{e^{-4}4^x/x!} =$
$\displaystyle \binom{x}{x_1}\left(\frac{1}{2}\right)^x \left(1 - \frac{1}{2}\right)^{x - x_1}.$

4.2.25 a) Yes, because the Poisson assumptions are probably satisfied—crashes are independent events and the crash rate is likely to remain constant.

b) Since $\lambda = 2.5$ crashes per year, $P(X \geq 4) = 1 - P(X \leq 3) = 1 - \displaystyle\sum_{k=0}^{3} \dfrac{e^{-2.5}(2.5)^k}{k!} = 0.24$.

c) Let Y = interval (in yrs.) between next two crashes. By Theorem 4.2.3, $P(Y < 0.25) = \displaystyle\int_0^{0.25} 2.5e^{-2.5y}dy = 1 - 0.535 = 0.465$.

4.2.27 Given that $f_Y(y) = 0.027e^{-0.027}$, $P(Y_1 + Y_2 < 40) = \displaystyle\int_0^{40}(0.027)^2 ye^{-0.027y}dy = \int_0^{1.08} ue^{-u}du = $
$e^{-u}(-u - 1) \Big|_0^{1.08} = 1 - 0.706 = 0.29$ (where $u = 0.027y$).

Section 4.3

4.3.1 a) 0.5782   b) 0.8264   c) 0.9306   d) 0.0000

4.3.3 a) Both are the same because of the symmetry of $f_Z(z)$.

b) Since $f_Z(z)$ is decreasing for all $z > 0$, $\displaystyle\int_{a - \frac{1}{2}}^{a + \frac{1}{2}} \dfrac{1}{\sqrt{2\pi}} e^{-z^2/2}dz$ is larger than

$\displaystyle\int_a^{a+1} \dfrac{1}{\sqrt{2\pi}} e^{-z^2/2}dz$.

4.3.5 a) −0.44   b) 0.76   c) 0.41   d) 1.28   e) 0.95

4.3.7 a) $\displaystyle\sum_{k=241}^{260}\binom{260}{k}(0.90)^k(0.10)^{260-k}$

b) Let X = number of ticket-holders who show up. Since $np = 260(0.90) = 234$ and $np(1-p) = 260(0.90)(0.10) = 23.4$ (and using the continuity correction on p. 268), $P(\text{plane is overbooked}) = P(241 \le X \le 260) = P(240.5 \le X \le 260.5) =$

$$P\left(\frac{240.5-234}{\sqrt{23.4}} \le \frac{X-234}{\sqrt{23.4}} \le \frac{260.5-234}{\sqrt{23.4}}\right) \doteq P(1.34 \le Z \le 5.48) = 0.0901.$$

4.3.9 Let X = number of voters challenger receives. Given that $n = 400$ and $p = P(\text{voter favors challenger}) = 0.45$, $np = 180$ and $np(1-p) = 99$.

a) $P(\text{tie}) = P(X = 200) = P(199.5 \le X \le 200.5) =$

$$P\left(\frac{199.5-180}{\sqrt{99}} \le \frac{X-180}{\sqrt{99}} \le \frac{200.5-180}{\sqrt{99}}\right) \doteq P(1.96 \le Z \le 2.06) = 0.0053.$$

b) $P(\text{challenger wins}) = P(X > 200) = P(X \ge 200.5) =$

$$P\left(\frac{X-180}{\sqrt{99}} \ge \frac{200.5-180}{\sqrt{99}}\right) \doteq P(Z \ge 2.06) = 0.0197.$$

4.3.11 Let $p = P(\text{person dies by chance in the three months following birthmonth}) = \dfrac{1}{4}$. Given that $n = 747$, $np = 186.75$, and $np(1-p) = 140.06$, $P(X \ge 344) = P(X \ge 343.5) =$

$$P\left(\frac{X-186.75}{\sqrt{140.06}} \ge \frac{343.5-186.75}{\sqrt{140.06}}\right) = P(Z \ge 13.25) = 0.0000.$$ The fact that the latter probability is so small strongly discredits the hypothesis that people die randomly with respect to their birthdays.

4.3.13 No, the normal approximation is inappropriate because the values of n (= 10) and p (= 0.7) fail to satisfy Condition (2) specified in the Comment on p. 268.

4.3.15 a) Since $E(X) = 200\left(\dfrac{1}{2}\right) = 100$ and $\text{Var}(X) = 200\left(\dfrac{1}{2}\right)\left(\dfrac{1}{2}\right) = 50$,

$P(|X - E(X)| < 5) > 1 - \dfrac{50}{25}$, so, in effect, the Chebyshev lower bound for $P(|X - E(X)| < 5)$ is 0.

b) $P(|X - E(X)| \le 5) = P(-5 \le X - 100 \le 5) = P\left(\dfrac{-5.5}{\sqrt{50}} \le \dfrac{X-100}{\sqrt{50}} \le \dfrac{5.5}{\sqrt{50}}\right) \doteq$

$P(-0.78 \le Z \le 0.78) = 0.5646.$

4.3.17 Let X_i = face showing on ith die, $i = 1, 2, ..., 100$, and let $X = X_1 + X_2 + ... + X_{100}$. Following the approach taken in Example 3.11.3 gives $E(X) = 350$. Also, $\text{Var}(X_i) = E(X_i^2) - [E(X_i)]^2 = \frac{1}{6}(1^2 + 2^2 + 3^2 + 4^2 + 5^2 + 6^2) - \left(3\frac{1}{2}\right)^2 = \frac{35}{12}$, so $\text{Var}(X) = \frac{3500}{12}$. By the central limit theorem, then, $P(X \geq 370) = P(X \geq 371) = P(X \geq 370.5) = P\left(\frac{X - 350}{\sqrt{3500/12}} \geq \frac{370.5 - 350}{\sqrt{3500/12}}\right) \doteq P(Z \geq 1.20) = 0.1151$.

4.3.19 Let X = number of chips ordered next week. Given that $\lambda = E(X) = 50$, P(company is unable to fill orders) $= P(X \geq 61) = P(X \geq 60.5) = P\left(\frac{X - 50}{\sqrt{50}} \geq \frac{60.5 - 50}{\sqrt{50}}\right) \doteq P(Z \geq 1.48) = 0.0694$.

4.3.21 No, only 84% of drivers are likely to get at least 25,000 miles on the tires. If X denotes the mileage obtained on a set of Econo-Tires, $P(X \geq 25,000) = P\left(\frac{X - 30,000}{5000} \geq \frac{25,000 - 30,000}{5000}\right) = P(Z \geq -1.00) = 0.8413$.

4.3.23 Let Y = donations collected tomorrow. Given that $\mu = \$20,000$ and $\sigma = \$5,000$, $P(Y > \$30,000) = P\left(\frac{Y - \$20,000}{\$5,000} > \frac{\$30,000 - \$20,000}{\$5,000}\right) = P(Z > 2.00) = 0.0228$.

4.3.25 a) Let Y_1 and Y_2 denote the scores made by a random nondelinquent and delinquent, respectively. Then $E(Y_1) = 60$ and $\text{Var}(Y_1) = 10^2$; also, $E(Y_2) = 80$ and $\text{Var}(Y_2) = 5^2$. Since 75 is the cutoff between teenagers classified as delinquents or nondelinquents, P(nondelinquent is misclassified as delinquent) $= P(Y_1 > 75) = P\left(Z > \frac{75 - 60}{10}\right) = 0.0668$. Similarly, P(delinquent is misclassified as nondelinquent) $= P(Y_2 < 75) = P\left(Z < \frac{75 - 80}{5}\right) = 0.1587$.

4.3.27 Let Y = freshman's verbal SAT score. Given that $\mu = 565$ and $\sigma = 75$, $P(Y > 660) = P\left(\frac{Y - 565}{75} > \frac{660 - 565}{75}\right) = P(Z > 1.27) = 0.1020$. It follows that the expected <u>number</u> doing better is 4250(0.1020), or 434.

4.3.29 If $P(20 \leq Y \leq 60) = 0.50$, then $P\left(\frac{20 - 40}{\sigma} \leq \frac{Y - 40}{\sigma} \leq \frac{60 - 40}{\sigma}\right) = 0.50 = P\left(\frac{-20}{\sigma} \leq Z \leq \frac{20}{\sigma}\right)$. But $P(-0.67 \leq Z \leq 0.67) = 0.4972 \doteq 0.50$, which implies that $0.67 = \frac{20}{\sigma}$. The desired value for σ, then, is $\frac{20}{0.67}$, or 29.85.

4.3.31 Let Y = analyzer reading for driver whose true blood alcohol concentration is 0.11. Then
P(analyzer mistakenly shows driver to be sober) = $P(Y < 0.10) = P\left(\dfrac{Y - 0.11}{0.004} < \dfrac{0.10 - 0.11}{0.004}\right) =$
$P(Z < -2.50) = 0.0062$. The "0.095%" driver should ask to take the test twice. The "0.11" driver has a greater chance of not being charged by taking the test only once. As n, the number of times the test is taken, increases, the precision of the average reading increases. It is to the sober driver's advantage to have a reading as precise as possible; the opposite is true for the drunk driver.

4.3.33 Since $Z = \dfrac{Y - \mu}{\sigma}$, $Y = \mu + \sigma z$. From Theorem 3.16.3, $M_Y(t) = e^{\mu t}M_Z(\sigma t) = e^{\mu t} \cdot e^{\sigma^2 t^2 / 2} =$
$e^{\mu t + \sigma^2 t^2 / 2}$, but the latter is the moment-generating function for a normal random variable with mean μ and variance σ^2.

4.3.35 $M_Y^{(1)}(t) = e^{\mu t + \sigma^2 t^2 / 2} \cdot [\mu + \sigma^2 t]$ and $M_Y^{(2)}(t) = e^{\mu t + \sigma^2 t^2 / 2} + e^{\mu t + \sigma^2 t^2 / 2}[\mu + \sigma^2 t]^2$. Therefore,
$E(Y) = M_Y^{(1)}(0) = \mu$ and $\mathrm{Var}(Y) = M_Y^{(2)}(0) - \left[M_Y^{(1)}(0)\right]^2 = \sigma^2 + \mu^2 - \mu^2 = \sigma^2$.

4.3.37 If $P(1.9 \le \bar{Y} \le 2.1) \ge 0.99$, then $P\left(\dfrac{1.9 - 2}{2/\sqrt{n}} \le Z \le \dfrac{2.1 - 2}{2/\sqrt{n}}\right) \ge 0.99$. But $P(-2.58 \le Z \le 2.58) \doteq$
0.99, so $2.58 = \dfrac{2.1 - 2}{2/\sqrt{n}}$, which implies that $n = 2663$.

4.3.39 Let Y_P and Y_C denote a random piston diameter and cylinder diameter, respectively. Then
P(pair needs to be reworked) = $P(Y_P > Y_C) = P(Y_P - Y_C > 0) =$
$P\left(\dfrac{Y_P - Y_C - (40.5 - 41.5)}{\sqrt{(0.3)^2 + (0.4)^2}} > \dfrac{0 - (40.5 - 41.5)}{\sqrt{(0.3)^2 - (0.4)^2}}\right) = P(Z > 2.00) = 0.0228$, or 2.28%.

Section 4.4

4.4.1 Let $p = P$(return is audited in a given year) = 0.30 and let X = year of first audit. Then
P(Jody escapes detection for at least 3 years) = $P(X \ge 4) = 1 - P(X \le 3) =$
$1 - \displaystyle\sum_{k=1}^{3}(0.70)^{k-1}(0.30) = 0.343$.

4.4.3   No, the expected frequencies (= $5 \cdot p_X(k)$) differ considerably from the observed frequencies, especially for small values of k. The observed number of 1's, for example, is 4, while the expected number is 12.5.

k	Obs. Freq.	$p_X(k) = \left(\dfrac{3}{4}\right)^{k-1}\left(\dfrac{1}{4}\right)$	$50 \cdot p_X(k) =$ Exp. freq.
1	4	0.2500	12.5
2	13	0.1875	9.4
3	10	0.1406	7.0
4	7	0.1055	5.3
5	5	0.0791	4.0
6	4	0.0593	3.0
7	3	0.0445	2.2
8	3	0.0334	1.7
9+	1	0.1001	5.0
	50	1.0000	50

4.4.5 $F_X(t) = P(X \le t) = p\displaystyle\sum_{s=0}^{[t]}(1-p)^s$. But $\displaystyle\sum_{s=0}^{[t]}(1-p)^s = \dfrac{1-(1-p)^{[t]}}{1-(1-p)} = \dfrac{1-(1-p)^{[t]}}{p}$, and the result follows.

4.4.7   No, because $M_X(t) = M_{X_1}(t) \cdot M_{X_2}(t)$ does not have the form of a geometric moment-generating function.

4.4.9   Let the random variable X^* denote the number of trials preceding the first success. By inspection, $p_{X^*}(t) = (1-p)^k p$, $k = 0, 1, 2, \ldots$ Also, $M_{X^*}(t) = \displaystyle\sum_{k=0}^{\infty} e^{tk} \cdot (1-p)^k\, p =$

$p\displaystyle\sum_{k=0}^{\infty}[(1-p)e^t]^k = p \cdot \left(\dfrac{1}{1-(1-p)e^t}\right) = \dfrac{p}{1-(1-p)e^t}$. Let X denote the geometric random variable defined in Theorem 4.4.1. Then $X^* = X - 1$, and $M_{X^*}(t) = e^{-t}M_X(t) =$

$e^{-t} \cdot \dfrac{pe^t}{1-(1-p)e^t} = \dfrac{p}{1-(1-p)e^t}$.

Section 4.5

4.5.1   Let X = number of houses needed to achieve fifth invitation. If $p = P$(saleswoman receives invitation at a given house) $= 0.30$, $p_X(k) = \dbinom{k-1}{4}(0.30)^4(0.70)^{k-1-4}(0.30)$, $k = 5, 6, \ldots$ and

$P(X < 8) = P(5 \le X \le 7) = \displaystyle\sum_{k=5}^{7}\dbinom{k-1}{4}(0.30)^5(0.70)^{k-5} = 0.029$.

4.5.3 Darryl might have actually done his homework, but there is reason to suspect that he did not. Let the random variable X denote the toss where a head appears for the second time. Then

$$p_X(k) = \binom{k-1}{1}\left(\frac{1}{2}\right)^2\left(\frac{1}{2}\right)^{k-2}, k = 2, 3, \ldots,$$ but that particular model fits the data almost

perfectly, as the table shows. Agreement this good is often an indication that the data have been fabricated.

k	$p_X(k)$	Obs. freq.	Exp. freq.
2	1/4	24	25
3	2/8	26	25
4	3/16	19	19
5	4/32	13	12
6	5/64	8	8
7	6/128	5	5
8	7/256	3	3
9	8/512	1	2
10	9/1024	1	1

4.5.5 Let Y denote the number of trials to get the rth success, and let X denote the number of trials in excess of r to get the rth success. Then $X = Y - r$. Substituting into Theorem 4.5.1 gives

$$p_X(k) = \binom{k+r-1}{r-1}p^r(1-p)^k = \binom{k+r-1}{k}p^r(1-p)^k, k = 0, 1, 2, \ldots$$

4.5.7 $M_X^{(1)}(t) = r\left[\dfrac{pe^t}{1-(1-p)e^t}\right]^{r-1}[pe^t[1-(1-p)e^t]^{-2}(1-p)e^t + [1-(1-p)e^t]^{-1}pe^t]$. When $t = 0$,

$$M_X^{(1)}(0) = E(X) = r\left[\frac{p(1-p)}{p^2}+\frac{p}{p}\right] = \frac{r}{p}.$$

4.5.9 $E(X) = \displaystyle\sum_{k=r}^{\infty} k\binom{k-1}{r-1}p^r(1-p)^{k-r} = \frac{r}{p}\sum_{k=r}^{\infty}\binom{k}{r}p^{r+1}(1-p)^{k-r} = \frac{r}{p}.$

Section 4.6

4.6.1 Consider the integral $Q = \displaystyle\int_0^\infty \lambda^r y^{r-1}e^{-\lambda y}dy$. Let $u = \lambda y$, so $du = \lambda dy$. Then $Q = \displaystyle\int_0^\infty u^{r-1}e^{-u}du$.

If r is a positive integer, $Q = (r-1)!$. Therefore, $\displaystyle\int_0^\infty \frac{\lambda^r}{(r-1)!}y^{r-1}e^{-\lambda y}dy = 1$.

4.6.3 The 11 Y_i's comprising Y are exponential random variables, each of which is sharply skewed. In general, the convergence of sums of skewed random variables to the standard normal is slower than it is for variables whose distributions are more nearly symmetric.

4.6.5 $E(Y^m) = \int_0^\infty y^m \cdot \dfrac{\lambda^r}{(r-1)!} y^{r-1} e^{-\lambda y} dy = \int_0^\infty \dfrac{\lambda^r}{(r-1)!} y^{m+r-1} e^{-\lambda y} dy =$

$\dfrac{(m+r-1)!}{\lambda^m (r-1)!} \int_0^\infty \dfrac{\lambda^{m+r}}{(m+r-1)!} y^{m+r-1} e^{-\lambda y} dy = \dfrac{(m+r-1)!}{\lambda^m (r-1)!} .$

4.6.7   a) $\Gamma(1) = \int_0^\infty e^{-y} dy = -e^{-y} \Big|_0^\infty = 1$

b) $\Gamma(r+1) = \int_0^\infty y^r e^{-y} dy$. Let $u = y^r$ and $dv = e^{-y} dy$.

Integrating by parts shows that $\Gamma(r+1) = r \int_0^\infty y^{r-1} e^{-y} dy$, but the latter is $r\Gamma(r)$.

c)   Let Z be a standard normal random variable. Then $E(Z^2) = \dfrac{1}{\sqrt{2\pi}} \int_{-\infty}^\infty z^2 e^{-z^2/2} dz =$

$\sqrt{\dfrac{2}{\pi}} \int_0^\infty z^2 e^{-z^2/2} dz = 1$. Let $y = z^2$. Then $E(Z^2) = \dfrac{2}{\sqrt{\pi}} \Gamma\left(1 + \dfrac{1}{2}\right) = \dfrac{2}{\sqrt{\pi}}\left(\dfrac{1}{2}\right)\Gamma\left(\dfrac{1}{2}\right)$, which

implies that $\Gamma\left(\dfrac{1}{2}\right) = \sqrt{\pi}$.

Chapter 5

Section 5.2

5.2.1 $L(\theta) = \prod_{i=1}^{8} \theta^{k_i}(1-\theta)^{1-k_i} = \theta^{\sum_{i=1}^{8} k_i}(1-\theta)^{8-\sum_{i=1}^{8} k_i} = \theta^5(1-\theta)^3$

$\dfrac{dL(\theta)}{d\theta} = \theta^5 3(1-\theta)^2(-1) + 5\theta^4(1-\theta)^3 = \theta^4(1-\theta)^2(-8\theta+5) \cdot \dfrac{dL(\theta)}{d\theta} = 0$ implies $\hat{\theta} = 5/8$

5.2.3 $L(\theta) = \prod_{i=1}^{4} \lambda e^{-\lambda y_i} = \lambda^4 e^{-\lambda \sum_{i=1}^{4} y_i} = \lambda^4 e^{-32.8\lambda}.$

$\dfrac{dL(\lambda)}{d\lambda} = \lambda^4(-32.8)e^{-32.8\lambda} + 4\lambda^3 e^{-32.8\lambda} = \lambda^3 e^{-32.8\lambda}(4 - 32.8\lambda)$

$\dfrac{dL(\lambda)}{d\lambda} = 0$ implies $\hat{\lambda} = 4/32.8 = 0.122$

5.2.5 $L(\theta) = \prod_{i=1}^{3} \dfrac{y_i^3 e^{-y_i/\theta}}{6\theta^4} = \dfrac{\left(\prod_{i=1}^{3} y_i^3\right) e^{-\sum_{i=1}^{3} y_i/\theta}}{216\theta^{12}}.$

$\ln L(\theta) = \ln \prod_{i=1}^{3} y_i^3 - \dfrac{1}{\theta}\sum_{i=1}^{3} y_i - \ln 216 - 12 \ln \theta$

$\dfrac{d\ln L(\theta)}{d\theta} = \dfrac{1}{\theta^2}\sum_{i=1}^{3} y_i - \dfrac{12}{\theta} = \dfrac{\sum_{i=1}^{3} y_i - 12\theta}{\theta^2}$

or $\dfrac{d\ln L(\theta)}{d\theta} = 0$ implies $\dfrac{\sum_{i=1}^{3} y_i - 12\theta}{\theta^2} = \dfrac{8.8 - 12\theta}{\theta^2} = 0$

or $\hat{\theta} = 0.733$

5.2.7 $L(\theta) = \prod_{i=1}^{5} \theta y_i^{\theta-1} = \theta^5 \left(\prod_{i=1}^{5} y_i\right)^{\theta-1}.$

$\ln L(\theta) = 5 \ln \theta + (\theta - 1)\sum_{i=1}^{5} \ln y_i$

$\dfrac{d\ln L(\theta)}{d\theta} = \dfrac{5}{\theta} + \sum_{i=1}^{5} \ln y_i = \dfrac{5 + \theta\sum_{i=1}^{5} \ln y_i}{\theta}$

$\dfrac{d\ln L(\theta)}{d\theta} = 0$ implies $\dfrac{5 - 2.961\theta}{\theta} = 0$ or $\hat{\theta} = 1.69$

5.2.9 a) $L(\theta) = \left(\dfrac{1}{\theta}\right)^n$, if $0 \le y_1, y_2, \ldots, y_n \le \theta$, and 0 otherwise. Thus $\hat{\theta} = y_{\max}$, which for these data is 14.2.

b) $L(\theta) = \left(\dfrac{1}{\theta_2 - \theta_1}\right)^n$, if $\theta_1 \le y_1, y_2, \ldots, y_n \le \theta_2$, and 0 otherwise. Thus $\hat{\theta}_1 = y_{\min}$ and $\hat{\theta}_2 = y_{\max}$. For these data, $\hat{\theta}_1 = 1.8$, $\hat{\theta}_2 = 14.2$.

5.2.11 $L(\theta) = \prod\limits_{i=1}^{n} 2 y_i \theta^2 = 2^n \left(\prod\limits_{i=1}^{n} y_i \right) \theta^{2n}$, if $0 \le y_1, y_2, \ldots, y_n \le 1/\theta$, and 0 otherwise. To maximize $L(\theta)$ maximize θ. Since each $y_i \le 1/\theta$, then $\theta \le 1/y_i$ for $1 \le i \le n$. Thus, the maximum value for θ under these constraints is the minimum of the $1/y_i$, or $\hat{\theta} = 1/y_{\max}$.

5.2.13 Let $\theta = \sigma^2$, so $L(\theta) = \prod\limits_{i=1}^{n} \dfrac{1}{\sqrt{2\pi\theta}} e^{-\frac{1}{2}\frac{(y_i-\mu)^2}{\theta}} = 2\pi^{-n/2}\theta^{-n/2} e^{-\frac{1}{2}\frac{1}{\theta}\sum\limits_{i=1}^{n}(y_i-\mu)^2}$

$\ln L(\theta) = -\dfrac{n}{2}\ln 2\pi - \dfrac{n}{2}\ln\theta - \dfrac{1}{2}\dfrac{1}{\theta}\sum\limits_{i=1}^{n}(y_i-\mu)^2$

$\dfrac{d\ln L(\theta)}{d\theta} = -\dfrac{n}{2\theta} + \dfrac{1}{2}\dfrac{1}{\theta^2}\sum\limits_{i=1}^{n}(y_i-\mu)^2 = \dfrac{1}{2}\dfrac{-n\theta + \sum\limits_{i=1}^{n}(y_i-\mu)^2}{\theta^2}$

Setting $\theta = 0$ gives $\hat{\theta} = \hat{\sigma}^2 = \dfrac{1}{n}\sum\limits_{i=1}^{n}(y_i-\mu)^2$

5.2.15 $E(Y) = \int_0^1 y(\theta^2 + \theta)y^{\theta-1}(1-y)dy = (\theta^2 + \theta)\int_0^1 y^{\theta}(1-y)dy = \dfrac{\theta}{\theta+2}$. Set $\dfrac{\theta}{\theta+2} = \bar{y}$, which yields $\hat{\theta} = \dfrac{2\bar{y}}{1-\bar{y}}$

5.2.17 For Y exponential, $E(Y) = 1/\lambda$. Then $1/\lambda = \bar{y}$ implies $\hat{\lambda} = 1/\bar{y}$.

5.2.19 $E(Y) = \int_k^{\infty} y\theta k^{\theta}\left(\dfrac{1}{y_i}\right)^{\theta+1} dy = \theta k^{\theta}\int_k^{\infty} y^{-\theta}dy = \dfrac{\theta k}{\theta-1}$

Setting $\dfrac{\theta k}{\theta-1} = \bar{y}$ gives $\hat{\theta} = \bar{y}/(\bar{y}-k)$

5.2.21 $E(Y) = \mu$, so $\hat{\mu} = \bar{y}$. $E(Y^2) = \sigma^2 + \mu^2$. Then substitute $\hat{\mu} = \bar{y}$ into the equation for $E(Y^2)$ to obtain $\hat{\sigma}^2 + \bar{y}^2 = \dfrac{1}{n}\sum\limits_{i=1}^{n} y_i^2$ or $\hat{\sigma}^2 = \dfrac{1}{n}\sum\limits_{i=1}^{n} y_i^2 - \bar{y}^2$

5.2.23 From Chapter 4, $E(X) = 1/p$. Setting $1/p = \bar{x}$, gives $\hat{p} = \dfrac{1}{\bar{x}}$. For the given data, $\hat{p} = 0.479$.

The expected frequencies are:

x	Observed frequency	Expected frequency
1	132	119.8
2	52	62.4
3	34	32.5
4	9	16.9
5	7	8.8
6	5	4.6
7	5	2.4
≥ 8	6	2.6

Section 5.3

5.3.1 The confidence interval is $\left(\bar{y} - z_{\alpha/2} \dfrac{\sigma}{\sqrt{n}}, \bar{y} + z_{\alpha/2} \dfrac{\sigma}{\sqrt{n}} \right) =$

$\left(0.766 - 1.96 \dfrac{0.09}{\sqrt{19}}, 0.766 + 1.96 \dfrac{0.09}{\sqrt{19}} \right) = (0.726, 0.806).$

The value of 0.80 is believable.

5.3.3 The length of the confidence interval is

$2 z_{\alpha/2} \dfrac{\sigma}{\sqrt{n}} = \dfrac{2(1.96)(14.3)}{\sqrt{n}} = \dfrac{56.056}{\sqrt{n}}$. For $\dfrac{56.056}{\sqrt{n}} \leq 3.06$, $n \geq \left(\dfrac{56.056}{3.06} \right)^2 = 335.58$, so take

$n = 336.$

5.3.5 The probability that the given interval will contain μ is $P(-0.96 < Z < 1.06) = 0.6869$. The probability of four or five such intervals is binomial with $n = 5$ and $p = 0.6869$, so the probability is $5(0.6869)^4(0.3131) + (0.6869)^5 = 0.501$.

5.3.7 The interval given is correctly *calculated*. However, the data do not appear to be normal, so claiming that it is a 95% confidence interval would not be correct.

5.3.9 $\left(\dfrac{192}{540} - 1.96 \sqrt{\dfrac{(192/540)(1 - 192/540)}{540}}, \dfrac{192}{540} + 1.96 \sqrt{\dfrac{(192/540)(1 - 192/540)}{540}} \right)$

$= (0.316, 0.396)$

5.3.11 Budweiser would use the sample proportion 0.54 alone as the estimate. Schlitz would construct the 95% confidence interval (0.36, 0.56) to claim that values < 0.50 are believable.

5.3.13 $2.58 \sqrt{\dfrac{p(1-p)}{n}} \leq 2.58 \sqrt{\dfrac{1}{4n}} \leq 0.01$, so take $n \geq \dfrac{(2.58)^2}{4(0.01)^2} = 16{,}641$

5.3.15 Both intervals have confidence level approximately 50%.

5.3.17 $\dfrac{z_\alpha}{2\sqrt{1013}} = \dfrac{3.1}{100}$ implies $z_a = 1.97$. The margin of error is correct at the 95% level. For the given data, estimates of the percentage as small as $0.30 - 0.031 = 0.269$ or as large as $0.30 + 0.031 = 0.331$ are believable.

5.3.19 If X is hypergeometric, then $\mathrm{Var}(X/n) = \dfrac{p(1-p)}{n}\dfrac{N-n}{N-1}$.

   As before $p(1-p) \le 1/4$. Thus, in Definition 5.3.1, substitute $d = \dfrac{1.96}{2\sqrt{n}}\sqrt{\dfrac{N-n}{N-1}}$.

5.3.21 If n is such that $0.06 = \dfrac{1.96}{2\sqrt{n}}$, then n is the smallest integer $\ge \dfrac{1.96^2}{4(0.06)^2} = 266.8$.
   Take $n = 267$.

   If n is such that $0.03 = \dfrac{1.96}{2\sqrt{n}}$, then n is the smallest integer $\ge \dfrac{1.96^2}{4(0.03)^2} = 1067.1$.
   Take $n = 1068$.

5.3.23 Case 1: n is the smallest integer greater than

   $\dfrac{z_{0.02}^2}{4(0.05)^2} = \dfrac{2.05^2}{4(0.05)^2} = 420.25$, so take $n = 421$.

   Case 2: n is the smallest integer greater than

   $\dfrac{z_{0.04}^2}{4(0.04)^2} = \dfrac{1.75^2}{4(0.04)^2} = 478.5$, so take $n = 479$.

5.3.25 Take n to be the smallest integer $\ge \dfrac{z_{0.10}^2}{4(0.02)^2} = \dfrac{1.28^2}{4(0.02)^2} = 1024$.

Section 5.4

5.4.1 $P(|\hat{\theta} - 3| > 1.0) = P(\hat{\theta} < 2) + P(\hat{\theta} > 4)$
   $= P(\hat{\theta} = 1.5) + P(\hat{\theta} = 4.5) = P((1,2)) + P((4,5)) = 2/10$

5.4.3 $P(X < 250 = P\left(\dfrac{X - 500(0.52)}{\sqrt{500(0.52)(0.48)}} < \dfrac{250 - 500(0.52)}{\sqrt{500(0.52)(0.48)}}\right) = P(Z < -0.90) = 0.1841$

5.4.5 a) $E(\overline{X}) = E\left(\dfrac{1}{n}\sum_{i=1}^{n} X_i\right) = \dfrac{1}{n}\sum_{i=1}^{n} E(X_i) = \dfrac{1}{n}\sum_{i=1}^{n}\lambda = \lambda$

   b) In general, the sample mean is an unbiased estimator of the mean μ.

5.4.7 a) $f_{Y_3'} = 12 \left(\dfrac{Y}{\theta} \right)^2 \left(1 - \dfrac{y}{\theta} \right) \dfrac{1}{\theta} = \dfrac{12}{\theta^4} [y^2(\theta - y)]$

$E(Y_3') = \dfrac{3}{5}\theta$, so the unbiased estimator is $\dfrac{5}{3} Y_3'$.

b) $\dfrac{5}{3} Y_3' = \dfrac{5}{3} 18 = 30$

c) Suppose the sample were 10, 14, 18, 31. The estimate for θ is 30, but the largest observation 31 falls outside of the [0, 30] interval.

5.4.9 $E(Y^2) = \displaystyle\int_0^\theta y^2 \dfrac{1}{\theta} dy = \dfrac{\theta^2}{3}$, so $3Y^2$ is unbiased.

5.4.11 $f_{\frac{n+1}{n} Y_{max}}(y) = \dfrac{n}{n+1} f_{Y_{max}} \left(\dfrac{n}{n+1} y \right) = \dfrac{n}{n+1} \dfrac{n}{\theta} \dfrac{n^{n-1}}{(n+1)^{n-1}} \dfrac{y^{n-1}}{\theta^{n-1}} = \dfrac{n^{n+1}}{(n+1)^n} \dfrac{y^{n-1}}{\theta^n}$

The median of this distribution is the number m such that

$$1/2 = \int_0^m \dfrac{n^{n+1}}{(n+1)^n} \dfrac{y^{n-1}}{\theta^n} dy = \dfrac{n^n}{(n+1)^n} \dfrac{y^n}{\theta^n} \bigg|_0^m = \dfrac{n^n}{(n+1)^n} \dfrac{m^n}{\theta^n}$$

Solving for m gives $m = \dfrac{1}{\sqrt[n]{2}} \dfrac{(n+1)}{n} \theta$. The estimator is unbiased only when $n = 1$.

5.4.13 $\hat{\theta}_n = \dfrac{1}{n} \displaystyle\sum_{i=1}^n (Y_i - \bar{Y})^2$, so $E(\hat{\theta}_n) = \dfrac{n-1}{n} \sigma^2$. This estimator is asymptotically unbiased since

$\displaystyle\lim_{n\to\infty} E(\hat{\theta}_n) = \lim_{n\to\infty} \dfrac{n-1}{n} \sigma^2 = \sigma^2$.

5.4.15 $\text{Var}\left(\dfrac{6}{5} \cdot Y_{max} \right) = \dfrac{\theta^2}{35}$, by Example 5.4.7.

$\text{Var}(Y_{max}) = \text{Var}\left(\dfrac{5}{6} \left(\dfrac{6}{5} Y_{max} \right) \right) = \dfrac{25}{36} \text{Var}\left(\dfrac{6}{5} Y_{max} \right) = \dfrac{25}{36} \dfrac{\theta^2}{35} = \dfrac{5\theta^2}{252}$.

By symmetry, $\text{Var}(Y_{min}) = \text{Var}(Y_{max})$.

$\text{Var}(6 \cdot Y_{min}) = 36 \text{Var}(Y_{min}) = 36 \dfrac{5\theta^2}{252} = \dfrac{5\theta^2}{7}$. Thus, $\dfrac{6}{5} \cdot Y_{max}$ has smaller variance. This result makes sense intuitively, since $\text{Var}(Y_{min}) = \text{Var}(Y_{max})$. Thus, efficiency here depends on the size of the constant needed to make the estimator unbiased.

5.4.17 $\text{Var}(\hat{\lambda}_1) = \text{Var}(X_1) = \lambda$. $\text{Var}(\hat{\lambda}_2) = \text{Var}(\bar{X}) = \lambda/n$.

$\text{Var}(\hat{\lambda}_2)/\text{Var}(\hat{\lambda}_1) = (\lambda/n)/\lambda = 1/n$

Section 5.5

5.5.1 $E(\hat{\theta}) = \dfrac{3}{2}E(\bar{Y}) = \dfrac{3}{2}E(Y) = \dfrac{3}{2}\left(\dfrac{2}{3}\theta\right) = \theta$

5.5.3 $\ln f_X(X;\lambda) = -\lambda + X\ln \lambda - \ln X!$

$\dfrac{\partial \ln f_X(X;\lambda)}{\partial \lambda} = -1 + X/\lambda$

$\dfrac{\partial^2 \ln f_X(X;\lambda)}{\partial \lambda^2} = -X/\lambda^2$

$E\left[\dfrac{\partial^2 \ln f_X(X;\lambda)}{\partial \lambda^2}\right] = -\lambda/\lambda^2 = -1/\lambda$, so the Cramer-Rao bound is λ/n. Also, $\text{Var}(\hat{\lambda}) = \text{Var}(\bar{X})$

$= \text{Var}(X)/n = \lambda/n$, so $\hat{\theta}$ is an efficient estimator.

5.5.5 $\ln f_Y(Y;\theta) = -\ln \theta$

$\dfrac{\partial \ln f_Y(Y;\theta)}{\partial \theta} = \dfrac{-1}{\theta}$

$E\left[\left(\dfrac{\partial \ln f_Y(Y;\theta)}{\partial \theta}\right)^2\right] = \dfrac{1}{\theta^2}$, so the Cramer-Rao bound is $\dfrac{\theta^2}{n}$. From Question 5.4.18,

$\text{Var}(\hat{\theta}) = \dfrac{\theta^2}{n(n+2)}$, which is smaller than the Cramer-Rao bound. This occurs because

Theorem 5.5.1 is not necessarily valid if the range of the pdf depends on the parameter.

5.5.7 $E\left(\dfrac{\partial^2 \ln f_W(W;\theta)}{\partial \theta^2}\right) = \displaystyle\int_{-\infty}^{\infty} \dfrac{\partial}{\partial \theta}\left(\dfrac{\partial \ln f_W(w;\theta)}{\partial \theta}\right) f_W(w;\theta)\, dw$

$= \displaystyle\int_{-\infty}^{\infty} \dfrac{\partial}{\partial \theta}\left(\dfrac{1}{f_W(w;\theta)}\dfrac{\partial f_W(w;\theta)}{\partial \theta}\right) f_W(w;\theta)\, dw$

$= \displaystyle\int_{-\infty}^{\infty}\left[\dfrac{1}{f_W(w;\theta)}\dfrac{\partial^2 f_W(w;\theta)}{\partial \theta^2} - \dfrac{1}{(f_W(w;\theta))^2}\left(\dfrac{\partial f_W(w;\theta)}{\partial \theta}\right)^2\right] f_W(w;\theta)\, dw$

$= \displaystyle\int_{-\infty}^{\infty}\dfrac{\partial^2 f_W(w;\theta)}{\partial \theta^2}\, dw - \int_{-\infty}^{\infty}\dfrac{1}{(f_W(w;\theta))^2}\left(\dfrac{\partial f_W(w;\theta)}{\partial \theta}\right)^2 f_W(w;\theta)\, dw$

$= 0 - \displaystyle\int_{-\infty}^{\infty}\left(\dfrac{\partial \ln f_W(w;\theta)}{\partial \theta}\right)^2 f_W(w;\theta)\, dw$

The 0 occurs because $1 = \displaystyle\int_{-\infty}^{\infty} f_W(w;\theta)\, dw$, so

$0 = \dfrac{\partial^2 \displaystyle\int_{-\infty}^{\infty} f_W(w;\theta)\, dw}{\partial \theta^2} = \displaystyle\int_{-\infty}^{\infty}\dfrac{\partial^2 f_W(w;\theta)}{\partial \theta^2}\, dw$

The above argument shows that

$$E\left(\frac{\partial^2 \ln f_W(W;\theta)}{\partial \theta^2}\right) = -E\left(\frac{\partial \ln f_W(W;\theta)}{\partial \theta}\right)^2$$

Multiplying both sides of the equality by n and inverting gives the desired equality.

Section 5.6

5.6.1 We already know that $\sum_{i=1}^{n} X_i$ is Poisson with parameter $n\lambda$. Thus $f_{\bar{X}}(\bar{x};\lambda) = \dfrac{e^{-n\lambda}(n\lambda)^{n\bar{x}}}{(n\bar{x})!}$ by Theorem 3.7.1.

$$\prod_{i=1}^{n}\frac{e^{-\lambda}\lambda^{x_i}}{x_i!} = \frac{e^{-n\lambda}\lambda^{\sum_{i=1}^{n}x_i}}{\prod_{i=1}^{n}x_i!} = \frac{e^{-n\lambda}\lambda^{n\bar{x}}n^{n\bar{x}}}{\left(\sum_{i=1}^{n}x_i\right)!}\frac{\left(\sum_{i=1}^{n}x_i\right)!}{\prod_{i=1}^{n}x_i!n^{n\bar{x}}}$$

$$= \frac{e^{-n\lambda}(n\lambda)^{n\bar{x}}}{(n\bar{x})!}\frac{\left(\sum_{i=1}^{n}x_i\right)}{\prod_{i=1}^{n}x_i!n^{n\bar{x}}} = f_{\bar{x}}(\bar{x};\lambda)s(x_1,x_2...,x_n)$$

By Theorem 5.6.1, $\bar{X}$ is sufficient.

5.6.3 $P((1, 1, 0)\,|\,X_1 + 2X_2 + 3X_3 = 3)$

$$= \frac{P((1, 1, 0) \text{ and } X_1 + 2X_2 + 3X_3 = 3)}{P(X_1 + 2X_2 + 3X_3 = 3)}$$

$$= \frac{P((1, 1, 0))}{P((1, 1, 0), (0, 0, 1))} = \frac{p^2(1-p)}{p^2(1-p) + p(1-p)^2} = p.$$

Since the conditional probability does depend on the parameter p, the statistic cannot be sufficient, by Definition 5.6.1.

5.6.5 $$\prod_{i=1}^{n} p_X(x_i;p) = \prod_{i=1}^{n}(1-p)^{x_i-1}p = (1-p)^{\left(\sum_{i=1}^{n}x_i\right)-n}p^n$$

Let $g\left(\sum_{i=1}^{n}x_i;p\right) = (1-p)^{\left(\sum_{i=1}^{n}x_i\right)-n}p^n$ and $u(x_1, \dots x_n) = 1$.

By Theorem 5.6.2, the statistic $\sum_{i=1}^{n} X_i$ is sufficient

5.6.7 $L = \prod_{i=1}^{n} f_Y(y_i; \theta) = \prod_{i=1}^{n} \theta y_i^{\theta-1} = \theta^n \left(\prod_{i=1}^{n} y_i \right)^{\theta-1}$, and

$$\ln L = n \cdot \ln \theta + (\theta - 1) \sum_{i=1}^{n} \ln y_i$$

$$\frac{d \ln L}{d\theta} = \frac{n}{\theta} + \sum_{i=1}^{n} \ln y_i$$

Setting $\frac{d \ln L}{d\theta} = 0$ gives $\hat{\theta} = \frac{-n}{\sum\limits_{i=1}^{n} \ln y_i} = \frac{-n}{\ln\left(\prod\limits_{i=1}^{n} y_i \right)}$, which is a function of $\prod\limits_{i=1}^{n} y_i$.

5.6.9 $\lambda e^{-\lambda y} = e^{\ln \lambda - \lambda y} = e^{y(-\lambda) + \ln \lambda}$. Take $K(y) = y$, $p(\lambda) = -\lambda$, $S(y) = 0$, and $q(\lambda) = \ln \lambda$. Then

$\hat{\theta} = \sum\limits_{i=1}^{n} k(y_i) = \sum\limits_{i=1}^{n} Y_i$, and $\sum\limits_{i=1}^{n} Y_i$ is sufficient.

Section 5.7

5.7.1 $P(16 < \bar{Y} < 20) = 0.90$ is equivalent to $P\left(\frac{16-18}{5.0/\sqrt{n}} < Z < \frac{20-18}{5.0/\sqrt{n}} \right) = 0.90$ or

$P(-0.40\sqrt{n} < Z < 0.40\sqrt{n}) = 0.90$. The $0.40\sqrt{n} = 1.64$ or $n = \left(\frac{1.64}{0.40} \right)^2 = 16.81$,

so take $n = 17$.

5.7.3 a) $P(Y_1 > 2\lambda) = \int_{2\lambda}^{\infty} \lambda e^{-\lambda y} dy = e^{-2\lambda^2}$. Then $P(|Y_1 - \lambda| < \lambda/2) < 1 - e^{-2\lambda^2} < 1$.

Thus, $\lim\limits_{n\to\infty} P(|Y_1 - \lambda|) < \lambda/2) < 1$.

b) $P\left(\sum\limits_{i=1}^{n} Y_i > 2\lambda \right) \geq P(Y_1 > 2\lambda) = e^{-2\lambda^2}$. The proof now proceeds along the lines of Part (a).

5.7.5 $E\left[(Y_{\max} - \theta)^2 \right] = \int_0^\theta (y - \theta)^2 \frac{n}{\theta} \left(\frac{y}{\theta} \right)^{n-1} dy$

$= \frac{n}{\theta^n} \int_0^\theta (y^{n+1} - 2\theta y^n + \theta^2 y^{n-1}) dy = \frac{n}{\theta^n} \left(\frac{\theta^{n+2}}{n+2} - \frac{2\theta^{n+2}}{n+1} + \frac{\theta^{n+2}}{n} \right)$

$= \left(\frac{n}{n+2} - \frac{2n}{n+1} + 1 \right) \theta^2$

Then $\lim\limits_{n\to\infty} E\left[(Y_{\max} - \theta)^2 \right] = \lim\limits_{n\to\infty} \left(\frac{n}{n+2} - \frac{2n}{n+1} + 1 \right) \theta^2 = 0$ and the estimator is squared error

consistent.

Chapter 6

Section 6.2

6.2.1 a) Reject H_0 if $\dfrac{\bar{y}-120}{18/\sqrt{25}} \leq -1.41$; $z = -1.61$; reject H_0.

b) Reject H_0 if $\dfrac{\bar{y}-42.9}{3.2/\sqrt{16}}$ is either 1) ≤ -2.58 or 2) ≥ 2.58; $z = 2.75$; reject H_0.

c) Reject H_0 if $\dfrac{\bar{y}-14.2}{4.1/\sqrt{9}} \geq 1.13$; $z = 1.17$; reject H_0.

6.2.3 a) No, because the observed z could fall <u>between</u> the 0.05 and 0.01 cutoffs.

b) Yes. If the observed z exceeded the 0.01 cutoff, it would necessarily exceed the 0.05 cutoff.

6.2.5 No, because two-sided cutoffs (for a given α) are further away from 0 that one-sided cutoffs.

6.2.7 a) H_0 should be rejected if $\dfrac{\bar{y}-12.6}{0.4/\sqrt{30}}$ is either **1)** ≤ -1.96 or **2)** ≥ 1.96. But $\bar{y} = 12.76$ and $z = 2.19$, suggesting that the machine should be readjusted.

b) The test assumes that the y_i's constitute a random sample from a normal distribution. Graphed, a histogram of the 30 y_i's shows a mostly bell-shaped pattern. There is no reason to suspect that the normality assumption is not being met.

6.2.9 P-value $= P(Z \leq -0.92) + P(Z \geq 0.92) = 0.3576$; H_0 would be rejected if α had been set at any value greater than or equal to 0.3576.

6.2.11 H_0 should be rejected if $\dfrac{\bar{y}-145.75}{9.50/\sqrt{25}}$ is either **1)** ≤ -1.96 or **2)** ≥ 1.96. Here, $\bar{y} = 149.75$ and $z = 2.10$, so the difference between \$145.75 and \$149.75 <u>is</u> statistically significant.

Section 6.3

6.3.1 a) Given that the technique worked $x = 24$ times during the $n = 52$ occasions it was tried, $z = \dfrac{24-52(0.40)}{\sqrt{52(0.40)(0.60)}} = 0.91$. The latter is not larger than $z_{.05} = 1.64$, so H_0: $p = 0.40$ would not be rejected at the $\alpha = 0.05$ level. These data do not provide convincing evidence that transmitting predator sounds helps to reduce the number of whales in fishing waters.

b) P-value $= P(Z \geq 0.91) = 0.1814$; H_0 would be rejected for any $\alpha \geq 0.1814$.

6.3.3 Let $p = P$(current supporter is male). Test H_0: $p = 0.65$ versus H_1: $p < 0.65$. Since $n = 120$ and $x =$ number of male supporters $= 72$, $z = \dfrac{72 - 120(0.65)}{\sqrt{120(0.65)(0.35)}} = -1.15$, which is not less than or equal to $-z_{.05}$ $(= -1.64)$, so H_0: $p = 0.65$ would not be rejected.

6.3.5 Let $p = P(Y_i \leq 0.69315)$. Test H_0: $p = \dfrac{1}{2}$ versus H_1: $p \neq \dfrac{1}{2}$. Given that $x = 26$ and $n = 60$, P-value $= P(X \leq 26) + P(X \geq 34) = 0.3030$.

6.3.7 Reject H_0 if $x \geq 4$ gives $\alpha = 0.50$; reject H_0 if $x \geq 5$ gives $\alpha = 0.23$; reject H_0 if $x \geq 6$ gives $\alpha = 0.06$; reject H_0 if $x \geq 7$ gives $\alpha = 0.01$.

6.3.9 a) $\alpha = P(\text{reject } H_0 \mid H_0 \text{ is true}) = P(X \leq 3 \mid p = 0.75) =$

$$\sum_{k=0}^{3} \binom{7}{k}(0.75)^k (0.25)^{7-k} = 0.07$$

b)

p	$P(X \leq 3 \mid p)$
0.75	0.07
0.65	0.20
0.55	0.39
0.45	0.61
0.35	0.80
0.25	0.93
0.15	0.99

Section 6.4

6.4.1 a) As described on p. 372, H_0: $\mu = 494$ is to be tested against H_1: $\mu \neq 494$ using ± 1.96 as the $\alpha = 0.05$ cutoffs. That is, H_0 is rejected if $\dfrac{\bar{y} - 494}{124/\sqrt{86}} \leq -1.96$ or if $\dfrac{\bar{y} - 494}{124/\sqrt{86}} \geq 1.96$. Equivalently, the null hypothesis is rejected if $\bar{y} \leq 467.8$ or if $\bar{y} \geq 520.2$. Therefore, $1 - \beta = P(\text{reject } H_0 \mid \mu = 500) = P(\bar{Y} \leq 467.8 \mid \mu = 500) + P(\bar{Y} \geq 520.2 \mid \mu = 500) =$

$$P\left(Z \leq \frac{467.8 - 500}{124/\sqrt{86}}\right) + P\left(Z \geq \frac{520.2 - 500}{124/\sqrt{86}}\right) = P(Z \leq -2.41) + P(Z \geq 1.51) =$$
$0.0080 + 0.0655 = 0.0735$.

6.4.3 The null hypothesis in Question 6.2.2 is rejected if $\bar{y}$ is either **1)** ≤ 89.0 or **2)** ≥ 101.0. Suppose $\mu = 90$. Since $\sigma = 15$ and $n = 22$, $1 - \beta = P(\bar{Y} \leq 89.0) + P(\bar{Y} \geq 101.0) =$

$$P\left(Z \leq \frac{89.0 - 90}{15/\sqrt{22}}\right) + P\left(Z \geq \frac{101.0 - 90}{15/\sqrt{22}}\right) = P(Z \leq -0.31) + P(Z \geq 3.44) = 0.3783 + 0.0003 =$$
0.3786.

6.4.5 H_0 should be rejected if $z = \dfrac{\bar{y} - 240}{50/\sqrt{25}} \le -2.33$ or , equivalently, if $\bar{y} \le 240 - 2.33 \cdot \dfrac{50}{\sqrt{25}} =$

216.7. Suppose $\mu = 220$. Then $\beta = P(\text{accept } H_0 \mid H_1 \text{ is true}) = P(\bar{Y} > 216.7 \mid \mu = 220) =$

$P\left(Z > \dfrac{216.7 - 220}{50/\sqrt{25}}\right) = P(Z > -0.33) = 0.6293.$

6.4.7 For $\alpha = 0.10$, H_0: $\mu = 200$ should be rejected if $\bar{y} \le 200 - 1.28 \cdot \dfrac{15.0}{\sqrt{n}}$. Also, $1 - \beta =$

$P\left(\bar{Y} \le 200 - 1.28 \cdot \dfrac{15.0}{\sqrt{n}} \,\Big|\, \mu = 197\right) = 0.75$, so $P\left(\dfrac{200 - 1.28 \cdot 15.0/\sqrt{n} - 197}{15.0/\sqrt{n}}\right) = 0.75.$ But

$P(Z \le 0.67) = 0.75$, implying that $\dfrac{200 - 1.28 \cdot 15.0/\sqrt{n} - 197}{15.0/\sqrt{n}} = 0.67.$ It follows that the

smallest n satisfying the conditions placed on α and $1 - \beta$ is 95.

6.4.9 Since H_1 is one-sided, H_0 is rejected when $\bar{y} \ge 30 + z_\alpha \cdot \dfrac{9}{\sqrt{16}}$. Also, $1 - \beta = \text{power} =$

$P\left(\bar{Y} \ge 30 + z_\alpha \cdot \dfrac{9}{\sqrt{16}} \,\Big|\, \mu = 34\right) = 0.85.$ Therefore, $1 - \beta = P\left(Z \ge \dfrac{30 + z_\alpha \cdot 9/\sqrt{16} - 34}{9/\sqrt{16}}\right) =$

0.85. But $P(Z \ge -1.04) = 0.85$, so $\dfrac{30 + z_\alpha \cdot 9/\sqrt{16} - 34}{9/\sqrt{16}} = -1.04$, implying that $z_\alpha = 0.74.$

Therefore, $\alpha = 0.23.$

6.4.11 In this context, α is the proportion of incorrect decisions made on innocent suspects—that is,

$\dfrac{9}{140}$, or 0.064. Similarly, β is the proportion of incorrect decisions made on guilty

suspects— here, $\dfrac{15}{140}$, or 0.107. A Type I error (convicting an innocent defendant) would

be considered more serious than a Type II error (acquitting a guilty defendant).

6.4.13 From the corollary on p. 182, $f_{Y_{\max}}(y) = \dfrac{5}{\theta}\left(\dfrac{y}{\theta}\right)^4$, $0 < y < \theta$ when $n = 5$. Therefore,

$\alpha = P(\text{reject } H_0 \mid H_0 \text{ is true}) = P(Y_{\max} \ge k \mid \theta = 2) = \int_k^2 \dfrac{5}{2}\left(\dfrac{y}{2}\right)^4 dy = 1 - \dfrac{k^5}{32}.$ For α to be 0.05,

$k = 1.98.$

6.4.15 $\beta = P(\text{accept } H_0 \mid H_1 \text{ is true}) = P(X \le n - 1 \mid p) = 1 - P(X = n \mid p) = 1 - \dbinom{n}{n} p^n (1 - p)^0 =$

$1 - p^n.$ When $\beta = 0.05$, $p = \sqrt[n]{0.95}.$

6.4.17 $1 - \beta = P(\text{reject } H_0 \mid H_1 \text{ is true}) = P\left(Y \le \dfrac{1}{2} \,\Big|\, \theta\right) = \int_0^{1/2} (1 + \theta) y^\theta dy = y^{\theta+1}\Big|_0^{1/2} = \left(\dfrac{1}{2}\right)^{\theta+1}.$

6.4.19 $P(\text{Type II error}) = \beta = P(\text{accept } H_0 \mid H_1 \text{ is true}) = P\left(X \le 3 \mid p = \dfrac{1}{2}\right) = \displaystyle\sum_{k=1}^{3}\left(1 - \dfrac{1}{2}\right)^{k-1} \cdot \dfrac{1}{2} = \dfrac{7}{8}$.

6.4.21 $\alpha = P(\text{reject } H_0 \mid H_0 \text{ is true}) = P(Y_1 + Y_2 \le k \mid \theta = 2)$. When H_0 is true, Y_1 and Y_2 are uniformly distributed over the square defined by $0 \le Y_1 \le 2$ and $0 \le Y_2 \le 2$, so the joint pdf of Y_1 and Y_2 is a plane parallel to the Y_1Y_2-axis at height $\dfrac{1}{4}\left(= f_{Y_1}(y_1) \cdot f_{Y_2}(y_2) = \dfrac{1}{2} \cdot \dfrac{1}{2}\right)$. By geometry, α is the volume of the triangular wedge in the lower left-hand corner of the square over which Y_1 and Y_2 are defined. The hypotenuse of the triangle in the Y_1Y_2-plane has the equation $y_1 + y_2 = k$. Therefore, $\alpha = \text{area of triangle} \times \text{height of wedge} = \dfrac{1}{2} \cdot k \cdot k \cdot \dfrac{1}{4} = k^2/8$. For α to be 0.05, $k = \sqrt{0.04} = 0.63$.

Section 6.5

6.5.1 $L(\hat{\omega}) = \displaystyle\prod_{i=1}^{n}(1 - p_0)^{k_i - 1} p_0 = p_0^n (1 - p_0)^{\sum_{i=1}^{n} k_i - n} = p_0^n (1 - p_0)^{k-n}$, where $k = \displaystyle\sum_{i=1}^{n} k_i$. From Example 5.2.1, the MLE for p is $\hat{p} = \dfrac{n}{k}$. Therefore, $L(\hat{\Omega}) = \left(\dfrac{n}{k}\right)^n \left(1 - \dfrac{n}{k}\right)^{k-n}$, and the generalized likelihood ratio for testing H_0: $p = p_0$ versus H_1: $p \ne p_0$ is the quotient $L(\hat{\omega})/L(\hat{\Omega})$.

6.5.3 $L(\hat{\omega}) = \displaystyle\prod_{i=1}^{n}(1/\sqrt{2\pi})e^{-\frac{1}{2}(y_i - \mu_0)^2} = (2\pi)^{-n/2}e^{-\frac{1}{2}\sum_{i=1}^{n}(y_i - \mu_0)^2}$. Since $\bar{y}$ is the MLE for μ (recall the first derivative taken in Example 5.2.4), $L(\hat{\Omega}) = (2\pi)^{-n/2}e^{-\frac{1}{2}\sum_{i=1}^{n}(y_i - \bar{y})^2}$. Here the generalized likelihood ratio reduces to $\lambda = L(\hat{\omega})/L(\hat{\Omega}) = e^{-\frac{1}{2}((\bar{y} - \mu_0)/(1/\sqrt{n}))^2}$. The null hypothesis should be rejected if $e^{-\frac{1}{2}((\bar{y} - \mu_0)/(1/\sqrt{n}))^2} \le \lambda^*$ or, equivalently, if $\left|(\bar{y} - \mu_0)\right|/(1/\sqrt{n}) > \lambda^{**}$, where values for λ^{**} come from the standard normal pdf, $f_Z(z)$.

6.5.5 a) $\lambda = \left(\dfrac{1}{2}\right)^n / [(x/n)^x (1 - x/n)^{n-x}] = 2^{-n}x^{-x}(n-x)^{x-n}n^n$. Rejecting H_0 when $0 < \lambda \le \lambda^*$ is equivalent to rejecting H_0 when $x\ln x + (n - x)\ln(n - x) \ge \lambda^{**}$.

b) By inspection, $x\ln x + (n - x)\ln(n - x)$ is symmetric in x. Therefore, the left-tail and right-tail critical regions will be equidistant from $p = \dfrac{1}{2}$, which implies that H_0 should be rejected if $\left|x - \dfrac{1}{2}\right| \ge k$, where k is a function of α.

Chapter 7

Section 7.2

7.2.1   a)   The true mean, μ, would be estimated by the sample mean, $\bar{y}$; here, $\hat{\mu} = \bar{y} = \dfrac{1}{10}\sum\limits_{i=1}^{10} y_i = $

0.48. The true variance, σ^2, would be estimated by the sample variance, s^2, where $s^2 = $

$$\frac{1}{10-1}\sum_{i=1}^{10}(y_i - 0.48)^2 = 0.058.$$

b) $P(Y > 0.5) = P\left(\dfrac{Y - 0.48}{\sqrt{0.058}} > \dfrac{0.5 - 0.048}{\sqrt{0.058}}\right) \doteq P(Z > 0.08) = 0.4681.$

7.2.3 $P(60.0 \le Y \le 61.0) = P\left(\dfrac{60.0 - 67.6}{2.58} \le \dfrac{Y - 67.6}{2.58} \le \dfrac{61.0 - 67.6}{2.58}\right) = P(-2.95 \le Z \le -2.56) = $

0.0036, so the expected number of recruits in the (60.0, 61.0) interval is $0.0036 \times 25{,}878$, or
93.2.

7.2.5 $f_Y(570) = \dfrac{1}{\sqrt{2\pi}(124)} e^{-\frac{1}{2}[(570-479)/124]^2} = 0.00246$; histogram height $=$

$$\frac{\text{class frequency}}{\text{sample size} \times \text{class width}} = \frac{118.8}{1050.4 \times 50} = 0.00226.$$

7.2.7 $\bar{y}_g = \dfrac{1}{825}[22(20) + 64(60) + \ldots + 3(300)] = \dfrac{1}{825}(120{,}780) = 146.4.$ Since $\sum\limits_{i=1}^{k} f_i m_i^2 = 22(20)^2 + $

$64(60)^2 + \ldots + 3(300)^2 = 19{,}971{,}600,\ \ s_g = \sqrt{\dfrac{825(19{,}971{,}600) - (120{,}780)^2}{825(824)}} = 52.71.$

Therefore, $P(Y \ge 100) = P(Y \ge 99.5) = P\left(\dfrac{Y - 146.4}{52.71} \ge \dfrac{99.5 - 146.4}{52.71}\right) \doteq P(Z \ge -0.89) = 0.8133,$

so the expected frequency is 825×0.8133, or 671.

7.2.9   The normal pdf, $f_Y(y;\sigma)$, can be written in exponential form, $f_Y(y;\sigma) = e^{K(y)p(\sigma) + S(y) + q(\sigma)}$, by

letting $K(y) = (y - \mu)^2$, $p(\sigma) = -\dfrac{1}{2\sigma^2}$, $S(y) = 0$, and $q(\sigma) = -\ln\!\left(\sqrt{2\pi}\sigma\right)$. It follows that

$$\sum_{i=1}^{n}(y_i - \mu)^2 = \sum_{i=1}^{n} K(y_i) \text{ is a sufficient statistic for } \sigma^2.$$

Section 7.3

7.3.1   a)   23.685   b)   4.605   c)   2.700

7.3.3 a) 2.088   b) 7.261   c) 14.041   d) 17.539

7.3.5 $\chi^2_{.95,200} \doteq 200\left(1 - \dfrac{2}{9(200)} + 1.64\sqrt{\dfrac{2}{9(200)}}\right)^3 = 233.9$

7.3.7 Subsituting $\dfrac{n}{2}$ and $\dfrac{1}{2}$ for r and λ, respectively, in the moment-generating function for a

gamma pdf gives $M_{\chi^2_n}(t) = (1 - 2t)^{-n/2}$. Also, $M^{(1)}_{\chi^2_n}(t) = (-n/2)(1 - 2t)^{-n/2 - 1}(-2) =$

$n(1 - 2t)^{-n/2 - 1}$ and $M^{(2)}_{\chi^2_n}(t) = \left(-\dfrac{n}{2} - 1\right)(n)(1 - 2t)^{-n/2 - 2}(-2) = (n^2 + 2n) \cdot (1 - 2t)^{-n/2 - 2}$, so

$M^{(1)}_{\chi^2_n}(0) = n$ and $M^{(2)}_{\chi^2_n}(0) = n^2 + 2n$. Therefore, $E(\chi^2_n) = n$ and $\mathrm{Var}(\chi^2_n) =$
$n^2 + 2n - n^2 = 2n$.

7.3.9 Let $Y = \chi^2_{200}$. Then $\dfrac{Y - 200}{\sqrt{400}} \doteq Z$, in which case $P\left(\dfrac{Y - 200}{\sqrt{400}} \le -0.25\right) \doteq 0.40$. Equivalently,

$Y \le 200 - 0.25\sqrt{400} = 195$, implying that $\chi^2_{.40,200} \doteq 195$.

7.3.11 $P\left(\dfrac{S^2}{\sigma^2} < 2\right) = P\left(\dfrac{(n-1)S^2}{\sigma^2} < 2(n-1)\right) = P\left(\chi^2_{n-1} < 2(n-1)\right)$. Values from the 0.95 column in a

χ^2 table show that for each $n < 8$, $P\left(\chi^2_{n-1} < 2(n-1)\right) < 0.95$. But for $n = 9$, $\chi^2_{.95,8} = 15.507$,
which means that $P\left(\chi^2_8 < 16\right) > 0.95$.

7.3.13 Since $E(S^2) = \sigma^2$, it follows from Chebyshev's inequality that $P(|S^2 - \sigma^2| < \varepsilon) >$

$1 - \dfrac{\mathrm{Var}(S^2)}{\varepsilon^2}$. But $\mathrm{Var}(S^2) = \dfrac{2\sigma^4}{n-1} \to 0$ as $n \to \infty$. Therefore, S^2 is consistent for σ^2.

7.3.15 If $n = 19$ and $\sigma^2 = 12.0$, $\dfrac{18S^2}{12.0}$ has a χ^2 distribution with 18 df, so

$P\left(8.231 \le \dfrac{18S^2}{12.0} \le 31.526\right) = 0.95 = P(5.49 \le S^2 \le 21.02)$.

7.3.17 Confidence intervals for σ (as opposed to σ^2) are often preferred by experimenters because
they are expressed in the same units as the data, which makes them easier to interpret.

7.3.19 H_0: $\sigma^2 = 1.1$ should be rejected in favor of H_1: $\sigma^2 < 1.1$ if $\dfrac{(6-1)S^2}{1.1} \le \chi^2_{.05,5} = 1.145$. But

$\displaystyle\sum_{i=1}^{6} y_i = 2641.8$, so $\bar{y} = \dfrac{2641.8}{6} = 440.3$ and $s^2 = \dfrac{1}{5}\displaystyle\sum_{i=1}^{6}(y_i - 440.3)^2 = 0.49$. Then

$\chi^2 = \dfrac{5(0.49)}{1.1} = 2.23$, implying that H_0 should not be rejected.

7.3.21 a) $M_Y(t) = \dfrac{1}{1 - \theta t}$. Let $X = \dfrac{2n\bar{Y}}{\theta} = \dfrac{2\sum\limits_{i=1}^{n} Y_i}{\theta}$. Then $M_X(t) = \prod\limits_{i=1}^{n} M_{Y_i}\left(\dfrac{2t}{\theta}\right) = \left(\dfrac{1}{1 - 2t}\right)^{2n/2}$,

implying that X is a χ^2_{2n} random variable.

b) $P\left(\chi^2_{\alpha/2, 2n} \leq \dfrac{2n\bar{Y}}{\theta} \leq \chi^2_{1-\alpha/2, 2n}\right) = 1 - \alpha$, so $\left(\dfrac{2n\bar{y}}{\chi^2_{1-\alpha/2, 2n}}, \dfrac{2n\bar{y}}{\chi^2_{\alpha/2, 2n}}\right)$ is a

$100(1 - \alpha)\%$ confidence interval for θ.

Section 7.4

7.4.1 a) 0.983   **b)** 0.132   **c)** 9.00

7.4.3 a) 6.23   **b)** 0.65   **c)** 9   **d)** 15
     e) 2.58

7.4.5 $F = \dfrac{U/m}{V/n}$, where U and V are independent χ^2 random variables with m and n degrees of

freedom, respectively. Then $\dfrac{1}{F} = \dfrac{V/n}{U/m}$, which implies that $\dfrac{1}{F}$ has an F distribution with n

and m degrees of freedom.

7.4.7 The 50 ratios constitute a random sample from an $F_{4,4}$ distribution. The 10th, 50th, and 90th percentiles of the data are 0.32, 1.24, and 3.72, respectively. By comparison, $F_{.10,4,4} = 0.243$, $F_{.50,4,4} = 1.00$, and $F_{.90,4,4} = 4.11$.

7.4.9 From Question 7.4.8, $E\left(\dfrac{U}{V}\right) = \dfrac{m}{n-2}$. But $E(F_{m,n}) = E\left(\dfrac{U/m}{V/n}\right) = \dfrac{n}{m} E\left(\dfrac{U}{V}\right) = \dfrac{n}{n-2}$

(for $n > 2$).

7.4.11 a) 2.508   **b)** −1.079   **c)** 1.7056   **d)** 4.3027

7.4.13 Since $\dfrac{\bar{Y} - 27.6}{S/\sqrt{9}}$ is a Student t random variable with 8 df, $P\left(-1.397 \leq \dfrac{\bar{Y} - 27.6}{S/\sqrt{9}} \leq 1.397\right) =$

0.80 and $P\left(-1.8595 \leq \dfrac{\bar{Y} - 27.6}{S/\sqrt{9}} \leq 1.8595\right) = 0.90$ (see Appendix Table A.2).

7.4.15 $P(90.6 - k(S) \leq \bar{Y} \leq 90.6 + k(S)) = 0.99 =$

$P\left(\dfrac{90.6 - k(S) - 90.6}{S/\sqrt{20}} \leq \dfrac{\bar{Y} - 90.6}{S/\sqrt{20}} \leq \dfrac{90.6 + k(S) - 90.6}{S/\sqrt{20}}\right) = P\left(\dfrac{k(S)}{S/\sqrt{20}} \leq T_{19} \leq \dfrac{k(S)}{S/\sqrt{20}}\right) =$

$P(-2.8609 \leq T_{19} \leq 2.8609)$, so $\dfrac{k(S)}{S/\sqrt{20}} = 2.8609$, implying that $k(S) = \dfrac{2.8609 \cdot S}{\sqrt{20}}$.

7.4.17 $\int_0^\infty \frac{1}{1+x^2}\,dx$ is the integral of the variable portion of a T_1 pdf over the upper half of its range.

Since $\int_0^\infty \dfrac{\Gamma(1)}{\sqrt{\pi}\,\Gamma\!\left(\frac{1}{2}\right)(1+t^2)}\,dt = \dfrac{1}{2}$, it follows that $\int_0^\infty \dfrac{1}{1+x^2}\,dx = \dfrac{1}{2}\cdot\dfrac{\Gamma\!\left(\frac{1}{2}\right)\sqrt{\pi}}{\Gamma(1)} = \dfrac{\pi}{2}$.

Section 7.5

7.5.1 Given that $n = 7$, $t_{\alpha/2,n-1} = t_{.025,6} = 2.4469$. Here $\bar{y} = \dfrac{1}{n}\sum_{i=1}^{n} y_i = \dfrac{1}{7}(12808) = 1829.71$, so the 95% confidence interval for μ reduces to

$$\left(1829.71 - 2.4469\cdot\frac{719.43}{\sqrt{7}},\ 1829.71 + 2.4469\cdot\frac{719.43}{\sqrt{7}}\right) = (\$1164,\ \$2495).$$

7.5.3 Let μ = true average daily fat intake of males in the age group 25 to 34. Since

$$\bar{y} = \frac{1}{10}(1101.3) = 110.13,\ s = \sqrt{\frac{10(128{,}428.67)-(1101.3)^2}{10(9)}} = 28.17,\ \text{and } t_{.05,9} = 1.8331,\ \text{the}$$

90% confidence interval for μ is $\left(110.13 - 1.8331\cdot\dfrac{28.17}{\sqrt{10}},\ 110.13 + 1.8331\cdot\dfrac{28.17}{\sqrt{10}}\right)$, which reduces to 93.80, 126.46).

7.5.5 There is no unique "right" answer here, but a reasonable strategy would be to construct an interval around $\bar{y}$ that would have a high probability of containing a future y_i. The endpoints of that interval would then serve as estimates for the lowest and highest returns likely to be realized. With $n = 30$, $\bar{y} = 14.2$, and $s = 2.4$, a __99%__ "prediction" interval for a future y_i would be $(14.2 - t_{.005,29}\cdot 2.4,\ 14.2 + t_{.005,29}\cdot 2.4)$, or $(7.6, 20.8)$.

7.5.7 No, because the length of a confidence interval for μ is a function of s as well as the confidence coefficient. If the sample standard deviation for the second sample was sufficiently small (relative to the sample standard deviation for the first sample), the 95% confidence interval would be shorter than the 90% confidence interval.

7.5.9 a)　0.95　　　　b)　0.80　　　　c)　0.945　　　　d)　0.95

7.5.11 Let μ = true average FEV$_1$/VC ratio for exposed workers. Since $\sum_{i=1}^{19} y_i = 14.56$ and

$\sum_{i=1}^{19} y_i^2 = 11.2904$, $\bar{y} = \dfrac{14.56}{19} = 0.766$ and $s = \sqrt{\dfrac{19(11.2904)-(14.56)^2}{19(18)}} = 0.0859$. To test H_0: $\mu = 0.80$ versus H_1: $\mu < 0.80$ at the $\alpha = 0.05$ level of significance, reject the null hypothesis if $t \le -t_{.05,18} = -1.7341$. But $t = \dfrac{0.766-0.80}{0.0859/\sqrt{19}} = -1.71$, so we fail to reject H_0.

7.5.13 Let μ = true average GMAT increase earned by students taking review course. The hypotheses to be tested are H_0: $\mu = 40$ versus H_1: $\mu < 40$. Here, $\sum_{i=1}^{15} y_i = 556$ and $\sum_{i=1}^{15} y_i^2 = 20{,}966$, so $\bar{y} = \dfrac{556}{15} = 37.1$, $s = \sqrt{\dfrac{15(20{,}966) - (556)^2}{15(14)}} = 5.0$, and $t = \dfrac{37.1 - 40}{5.0/\sqrt{15}} =$ -2.25. Since $-t_{.05,14} = -1.7613$, H_0 should be rejected at the $\alpha = 0.05$ level of significance, suggesting that the MBAs 'R Us advertisement may be fraudulent.

7.5.15 Let u = true average pit depth associated with plastic coating. To test H_0: $\mu = 0.0042$ versus H_1: $\mu < 0.0042$ at the $\alpha = 0.05$ level, we should reject the null hypothesis if $t \le -t_{.05,9} =$ -1.8331. For the 10 y_i's, $\bar{y} = \dfrac{0.0390}{10} = 0.0039$. Also, $s = 0.00383$, so $t = \dfrac{0.0039 - 0.0042}{0.00383/\sqrt{10}} =$ -2.48. Since H_0 is rejected , these data support the claim that the plastic coating is an effective corrosion retardant.

7.5.17 Because of the skewed shape of $f_Y(y)$, and if the sample size was small, it would not be unusual for all the y_i's to lie close together near 0. When that happens, $\bar{y}$ will be less than μ, s will be considerably smaller than $E(S)$, and the t ratio will be further to the left of 0 than $f_{T_{n-1}}(t)$ would predict.

7.5.19 As n increases, Student t pdfs converge to the standard normal, $f_Z(z)$ (see Question 7.4.16).

7.5.21 Let $\phi = \sqrt{\dfrac{n}{2}}(0.60)$ and $1 - \beta = 0.90$. The accompanying table, whose entries come from Figure 7.5.5, indicates that the smallest sample size capable of achieving the desired precision (when $\alpha = 0.05$) is $n = 32$.

n	ϕ	df	$1-\beta$
20	1.90	19	0.72
25	2.12	24	0.82
30	2.32	29	0.88
31	2.36	30	0.89
32	2.40	31	0.91

7.5.23 a) Let $\alpha = 0.05$, $\phi = \sqrt{\dfrac{n}{2}}(1.2)$, and $1 - \beta = 0.70$. From Figure 7.5.5 (using trial and error), we find that the smallest acceptable sample size is $n = 7$.

b) Let $\alpha = 0.01$, $\phi = \sqrt{\dfrac{n}{2}}(1.2)$, and $1 - \beta = 0.70$. Here, the left-hand set of curves in Figure 7.5.5 show that the minimum sample size is $n = 11$.

7.5.25 Let $\alpha = 0.01$ and $\phi = \sqrt{\dfrac{7}{2}}(2) = 3.74$. From Figure 7.5.5, $1 - \beta = 0.60$.

Chapter 8

Section 8.2

Chapter 9

Section 9.2

9.2.1 $\quad t = \dfrac{\bar{x} - \bar{y}}{s_p\sqrt{1/n + 1/m}} = \dfrac{65.2 - 75.5}{13.9\sqrt{1/9 + 1/12}} = -1.68$

Since $-t_{0.05,19} = -1.7291 < t = -1.68$, accept H_0.

9.2.3 $\quad s_p = \sqrt{\dfrac{(n-2)s_X^2 + (m-1)s_Y^2}{n + m - 2}} = \sqrt{\dfrac{5(167.568 + 11(52.072)}{6 + 12 - 2}} = 9.39.$

$\quad t = \dfrac{\bar{x} - \bar{y}}{s_p\sqrt{1/n + 1/m}} = \dfrac{28.6 - 12.758}{9.39\sqrt{1/6 + 1/12}} = 3.37$

Since $t = 3.37 > 2.9208 = t_{0.005,16}$, reject H_0.

9.2.5 $\quad s_p = \sqrt{\dfrac{7(7.169) + 7(10.304)}{8 + 8 - 2}} = 2.956$

$\quad t = \dfrac{11.2 - 9.7875}{2.956\sqrt{1/8 + 1/8}} = 0.96$

Since $t = 0.96 < t_{0.05,14} = 1.7613$, accept H_0.

9.2.7 $\quad$ Let $\alpha = 0.10$. $\quad s_p = \sqrt{\dfrac{99(600^2) + 49(700^2)}{100 + 50 - 2}} = 634.9$

$\quad t = \dfrac{2000 - 2500}{634.9\sqrt{1/100 + 1/50}} = -4.55$

Since $t = -4.55 < -t_{0.05,148} = -z_{0.05} = -1.64$, reject H_0

9.2.9 **a)** $\quad$ Reject H_0 if $t > t_{0.005,15} = 2.9467$, so we seek the smallest value of $|\bar{x} - \bar{y}|$ such that $t =$

$\qquad \dfrac{|\bar{x} - \bar{y}|}{s_p\sqrt{1/n + 1/m}} = \dfrac{|\bar{x} - \bar{y}|}{15.3\sqrt{1/6 + 1/11}} > 2.9467,$ or $|\bar{x} - \bar{y}| > (15.3)(0.508)(2.9467) =$

$\qquad 22.90$

b) $\quad$ Reject H_0 if $t > t_{0.05,19} = 1.7291$, so we seek the smallest value of $\bar{x} - \bar{y}$ such that

$\qquad t = \dfrac{\bar{x} - \bar{y}}{s_p\sqrt{1/n + 1/m}} = \dfrac{\bar{x} - \bar{y}}{214.9\sqrt{1/13 + 1/8}} > 1.7291,$ or $\bar{x} - \bar{y} > (214.9)(0.44936)(1.7291) =$

$\qquad 166.97$

9.2.11 **a)** $\quad$ Let X be the interstate route; Y, the town route.

$\qquad P(X > Y) = P(X - Y > 0).$ $\operatorname{Var}(X - Y) = \operatorname{Var}(X) + \operatorname{Var}(Y) = 6^2 + 5^2 = 61.$

$\qquad P(X - Y > 0) = P\left(\dfrac{X - Y - (33 - 35)}{\sqrt{61}} > \dfrac{2}{\sqrt{61}}\right)$

$\qquad = P(Z \geq 0.26) = 1 - 0.6026 = 0.3974$

b) $\text{Var}(\bar{X} - \bar{Y}) = \text{Var}(\bar{X}) + \text{Var}(\bar{Y}) = 6^2/10 + 5^2/10 = 61/10$

$$P(\bar{X} - \bar{Y}) > 0 = P\left(\frac{\bar{X} - \bar{Y} - (33 - 35)}{\sqrt{61/10}} > \frac{2}{\sqrt{61/10}}\right)$$

$$= P(Z > 0.81) = 1 - 0.7910 = 0.2090$$

9.2.13 $E(S_X^2) = E(S_Y^2) = \sigma^2$ by Example 5.4.4.

$$E(S_p^2) = \frac{(n-1)E(S_X^2) + (m-1)E(S_Y^2)}{n+m-2}$$

$$= \frac{(n-1)\sigma^2 + (m-1)\sigma^2}{n+m-2} = \sigma^2$$

9.2.15 For the data given, $\bar{x} = 545.45$, $s_X = 428$, and $\bar{y} = 241.82$, $s_Y = 183$. Then

$$t = \frac{\bar{x} - \bar{y}}{\sqrt{s_X^2/n + s_Y^2/m}} = \frac{545.45 - 241.82}{\sqrt{428^2/11 + 183^2/11}} = 2.16$$

The degrees of freedom associated with this statistic is the greatest integer in

$$\frac{\left(s_X^2/n + s_Y^2/m\right)^2}{\left(s_X^2/n\right)^2(n-1) + \left(s_Y^2/m\right)^2/(m-1)} = \frac{(428^2/11 + 183^2/11)^2}{(428^2/11)^2/10 + (183^2/11)^2/10} = 13.5.$$

The greatest integer is 13. Since $t = 2.16 > t_{0.05,13} = 1.7709$, reject H_0.

Section 9.3

9.3.1 a) The critical values are $F_{0.025,25,4}$ and $F_{0.975,25,4}$. These values are not tabulated, but in this case, we can approximate them by $F_{0.025,24,4} = 0.296$ and $F_{0.975,24,4} = 8.51$. The observed $F = 86.9/73.6 = 1.181$. Since $0.296 < 1.181 < 8.51$, we can accept H_0 that the variances are equal.

   b) Yes, we can use Theorem 9.2.2, since we have no reason to doubt that the variances are equal.

9.3.3 a) The critical values are $F_{0.025,19,19}$ and $F_{0.975,19,19}$. These values are not tabulated, but in this case, we can approximate them by $F_{0.025,20,20} = 0.406$ and $F_{0.975,20,20} = 2.46$. The observed $F = 2.41/3.52 = 0.685$. Since $0.406 < 0.685 < 2.46$, we can accept H_0 that the variances are equal.

   b) Since $t = 2.662 > t_{0.025,38} = 2.0244$, reject H_0.

9.3.5 $F = 0.20^2/0.37^2 = 0.292$. Since $F_{0.025,9,9} = 0.248 < 0.292 < 4.03 = F_{0.975,9,9}$, accept H_0.

9.3.7 Let $\alpha = 0.05$. $F = 65.25/227.77 = 0.286$. Since $0.208 = F_{0.025,8,5} < 0.286 < 6.76 = F_{0.975,8,5}$, accept H_0. Thus, Theorem 9.2.2 is appropriate.

9.3.9 If $\sigma_X^2 = \sigma_Y^2 = \sigma^2$, the maximum likelihood estimator for σ^2 is

$$\hat{\sigma}^2 = \frac{1}{n+m}\left(\sum_{i=1}^{n}(x_i - \bar{x})^2 + \sum_{i=1}^{m}(y_i - \bar{y})^2\right). \text{ Then}$$

$$L(\hat{\omega}) = \left(\frac{1}{2\pi\hat{\sigma}^2}\right)^{(n+m)/2} e^{-\frac{1}{2\hat{\sigma}^2}\left[\sum_{i=1}^{n}(x_i-\bar{x})^2 + \sum_{i=1}^{m}(y_i-\bar{y})^2\right]} = \left(\frac{1}{2\pi\hat{\sigma}^2}\right)^{(n+m)/2} e^{-(n+m)/2}$$

If $\sigma_X^2 \neq \sigma_Y^2$ the maximum likelihood estimators for σ_X^2 and σ_Y^2 are

$$\hat{\sigma}_X^2 = \frac{1}{n}\sum_{i=1}^{n}(x_i - \bar{x})^2, \text{ and } \hat{\sigma}_Y^2 = \frac{1}{m}\sum_{i=1}^{m}(y_i - \bar{y})^2.$$

Then $L(\hat{\Omega}) = \left(\frac{1}{2\pi\hat{\sigma}_X^2}\right)^{n/2} e^{-\frac{1}{2\hat{\sigma}_X^2}\left(\sum_{i=1}^{n}(x_i-\bar{x})^2\right)} \left(\frac{1}{2\pi\hat{\sigma}_Y^2}\right)^{m/2} e^{-\frac{1}{2\hat{\sigma}_Y^2}\left(\sum_{i=1}^{m}(y_i-\bar{y})^2\right)}$

$$= \left(\frac{1}{2\pi\hat{\sigma}_X^2}\right)^{n/2} e^{-m/2}\left(\frac{1}{2\pi\hat{\sigma}_Y^2}\right)^{m/2} e^{-n/2}$$

The ratio $\lambda = \dfrac{L(\hat{\omega})}{L(\hat{\Omega})} = \dfrac{(\hat{\sigma}_X^2)^{n/2}(\hat{\sigma}_Y^2)^{m/2}}{(\hat{\sigma}^2)^{(n+m)/2}}$, which equates to the expression given in the statement of the question.

Section 9.4

9.4.1 $\hat{p} = \dfrac{x+y}{n+m} = \dfrac{55+40}{200+200} = 0.2375$

$$z = \frac{\dfrac{x}{n} - \dfrac{y}{m}}{\sqrt{\dfrac{\hat{p}(1-\hat{p})}{n} + \dfrac{\hat{p}(1-\hat{p})}{m}}} = \frac{\dfrac{55}{200} - \dfrac{40}{200}}{\sqrt{\dfrac{0.2375(0.7625)}{200} + \dfrac{0.2375(0.7625)}{200}}} = 1.76$$

Since $-1.96 < z = 1.76 < 1.96 = z_{0.025}$, accept H_0.

9.4.3 Let $\alpha = 0.05$. $\hat{p} = \dfrac{24+27}{29+32} = 0.836$

$$z = \frac{\dfrac{24}{29} - \dfrac{27}{32}}{\sqrt{\dfrac{0.836(0.164)}{29} + \dfrac{0.836(0.164)}{32}}} = -0.17$$

For this experiment, H_0: $p_X = p_Y$ and H_1: $p_X \neq p_Y$. Since $-1.96 < z = -0.17 < 1.96 = z_{0.025}$, accept H_0 at the 0.05 level of significance.

9.4.5 $\hat{p} = \dfrac{60+48}{100+100} = 0.54$

$z = \dfrac{\dfrac{60}{100} - \dfrac{48}{100}}{\sqrt{\dfrac{0.54(0.46)}{100} + \dfrac{0.54(0.46)}{100}}} = 1.70$

The P value is $P(Z \leq -1.70) + P(Z \geq 1.70) = 2(1 - 0.9554) = 0.0892$.

9.4.7 $\hat{p} = \dfrac{175+100}{609+160} = 0.358$

$z = \dfrac{\dfrac{175}{609} - \dfrac{100}{160}}{\sqrt{\dfrac{0.358(0.642)}{609} + \dfrac{0.358(0.642)}{160}}} = -7.93$. Since $z = -7.93 < -1.96 = -z_{0.025}$, reject H_0.

9.4.9 From Equation 9.4.1,

$\lambda = \dfrac{[(55+60)/(160+192)]^{(55+60)}[1-(55+60)/(160+192)]^{(160+192-55-60)}}{(55/160)^{55}[1-(55/160)]^{105}(60/192)^{60}[1-(60/192)]^{132}}$

$= \dfrac{115^{115}(237^{237})(160^{160})(192^{192})}{352^{352}(55^{55})(105^{105})(60^{60})(132^{132})}$. We calculate $\ln \lambda$, which is -0.1935. Then $-2\ln \lambda =$

0.387. Since $-2\ln \lambda = 0.387 < 6.635 = \chi^2_{0.99,1}$, accept H_0.

Section 9.5

9.5.1 The center of the confidence interval is $\bar{x} - \bar{y} = 1007.9 - 831.9 = 176.0$. The radius is

$t_{\alpha/2, n+m-2} s_p \sqrt{\dfrac{1}{n} + \dfrac{1}{m}} = 2.0739(411)\sqrt{\dfrac{1}{9} + \dfrac{1}{15}} = 359.4$. The confidence interval is

$(176.0 - 359.4, 176.0 + 359.4) = (-183.4, 535.4)$

9.5.3 The center of the confidence interval is $\bar{x} - \bar{y} = 83.96 - 84.84 = -0.88$. The radius is

$t_{\alpha/2, n+m-2} s_p \sqrt{\dfrac{1}{n} + \dfrac{1}{m}} = 2.2281(11.2)\sqrt{\dfrac{1}{5} + \dfrac{1}{7}} = 14.61$. The confidence interval is $(-0.88 -$

$14.61, -0.88 + 14.61) = (-15.49, 13.73)$. Since the confidence interval contains 0, the data do not suggest that the dome makes a difference.

9.5.5 Equation (9.5.1) is $P\left(-t_{\alpha/2,n+m-2} \leq \dfrac{\overline{X}-\overline{Y}-(\mu_X-\mu_Y)}{S_p\sqrt{\dfrac{1}{n}+\dfrac{1}{m}}} \leq t_{\alpha/2,n+m-2}\right) = 1-\alpha$

which implies

$$P\left(-t_{\alpha/2,n+m-2}S_p\sqrt{\frac{1}{n}+\frac{1}{m}} \leq \overline{X}-\overline{Y}-(\mu_X-\mu_Y) \leq t_{\alpha/2,n+m-2}S_p\sqrt{\frac{1}{n}+\frac{1}{m}}\right) = 1-\alpha, \text{ or}$$

$$P\left(-(\overline{X}-\overline{Y})-t_{\alpha/2,n+m-2}S_p\sqrt{\frac{1}{n}+\frac{1}{m}} \leq -(\mu_X-\mu_Y) \leq -(\overline{X}-\overline{Y})+t_{\alpha/2,n+m-2}S_p\sqrt{\frac{1}{n}+\frac{1}{m}}\right)$$
$$= 1-\alpha$$

Multiplying the inequality above by -1 gives the inequality of the confidence interval of Theorem 9.5.1.

9.5.7 Approximate the needed $F_{0.025,25,4}$ and $F_{0.975,25,4}$ by $F_{0.025,24,4} = 0.296$ and $F_{0.975,24,4} = 8.51$. The confidence interval is approximately $\left(\dfrac{s_X^2}{s_Y^2}F_{0.025,24,4},\dfrac{s_X^2}{s_Y^2}F_{0.975,24,4}\right) =$

$\left(\dfrac{73.6}{86.9}(0.296),\dfrac{73.6}{86.9}(8.51)\right) = (0.251, 7.21)$. Because the confidence interval contains 1, it supports the conclusion of Question 9.3.1 to accept H_0 that the variances are equal.

9.5.9 Since $\dfrac{S_Y^2/\sigma_Y^2}{S_X^2/\sigma_X^2}$ has an F distribution with $m-1$ and $n-1$ degrees of freedom,

$$P\left(F_{\alpha/2,m-1,n-1} \leq \frac{S_Y^2/\sigma_Y^2}{S_X^2/\sigma_X^2} \leq F_{1-\alpha/2,m-1,n-1}\right) = 1-\alpha \text{ or}$$

$$P\left(\frac{S_X^2}{S_Y^2}F_{\alpha/2,m-1,n-1} \leq \frac{\sigma_X^2}{\sigma_Y^2} \leq \frac{S_X^2}{S_Y^2}F_{1-\alpha/2,m-1,n-1}\right) = 1-\alpha$$

The inequality provides the confidence interval of Theorem 9.5.2.

9.5.11 The approximate normal distribution implies that

$$P\left(-z_\alpha \leq \frac{\dfrac{X}{n}-\dfrac{Y}{m}-(p_X-p_Y)}{\sqrt{\dfrac{(X/n)(1-X/n)}{n}+\dfrac{(Y/m)(1-Y/m)}{m}}} \leq z_\alpha\right) = 1-\alpha$$

$$\text{or } P\left(-z_\alpha\sqrt{\frac{(X/n)(1-X/n)}{n}+\frac{(Y/m)(1-Y/m)}{m}} \leq \frac{X}{n}-\frac{Y}{m}-(p_X-p_Y)\right.$$

$$\left. \leq z_\alpha\sqrt{\frac{(X/n)(1-X/n)}{n}+\frac{(Y/m)(1-Y/m)}{m}}\right) = 1-\alpha$$

which implies that

$$P\left(-\left(\frac{X}{n}-\frac{Y}{m}\right)-z_\alpha\sqrt{\frac{(X/n)(1-X/n)}{n}+\frac{(Y/m)(1-Y/m)}{m}}\leq-(p_X-p_Y)\right.$$

$$\left.\leq-\left(\frac{X}{n}-\frac{Y}{M}\right)+z_\alpha\sqrt{\frac{(X/n)(1-X/n)}{n}+\frac{(Y/m)(1-Y/m)}{m}}\right)=1-\alpha$$

Multiplying the inequality by -1 yields the confidence interval.

Appendix 9.2

9.A.2.1 $\phi=\dfrac{\Delta}{\sigma}\dfrac{1}{\sqrt{1/n+1/m}}\dfrac{1}{\sqrt{2}}=(1.5)\dfrac{1}{\sqrt{1/4+1/6}}\dfrac{1}{\sqrt{2}}=1.64.$

$\nu=4+6-2=8$. From Figure 7.5.5, $1-\beta=0.52$, so $\beta=0.48$.

9.A.2.3 $\phi=\dfrac{\Delta}{\sigma}\dfrac{1}{\sqrt{1/n+1/m}}\dfrac{1}{\sqrt{2}}=(1.8)\dfrac{1}{\sqrt{1/8+1/14}}\dfrac{1}{\sqrt{2}}=2.87$

$\nu=8+14-2=20$. From Figure 7.5.5, $1-\beta=0.97$.

9.A.2.5 $\phi=\dfrac{\Delta}{\sigma}\dfrac{1}{\sqrt{1/n+1/n}}\dfrac{1}{\sqrt{2}}=(1.5)\sqrt{\dfrac{n}{4}}=0.75\sqrt{n}$. From trial and error using Figure 7.5.5, we

deduce that for $n\leq8$, $1-\beta\leq0.80$ and for $n=9$, $1-\beta=0.85$.

Chapter 10

Section 10.2

10.2.1 Let X_i = number of students with a score of i, $i = 1, 2, 3, 4, 5$. Then $P(X_1 = 0, X_2 = 0, X_3 = 1,$

$X_4 = 2, X_5 = 3) = \dfrac{6!}{0!0!1!2!3!} (0.116)^0(0.325)^0(0.236)^1(0.211)^2(0.112)^3 = 0.000886$.

10.2.3 Let Y denote a person's blood pressure and let X_1, X_2, and X_3 denote the number of individuals with blood pressures less than 140, between 140 and 160, and over 160, respectively. If $\mu = 124$ and $\sigma = 13.7$, $p_1 = P(Y < 140) = P\left(Z < \dfrac{140-124}{13.7}\right) = 0.8790$,

$p_2 = P(140 \le Y \le 160) = P\left(\dfrac{140-124}{13.7} \le Z \le \dfrac{160-124}{13.7}\right) = 0.1167$, and $p_3 = 1 - p_1 - p_2 =$

0.0043. Then $P(X_1 = 6, X_2 = 3, X_3 = 1) = \dfrac{10!}{6!3!1!}(0.8790)^6(0.1167)^3(0.0043)^1 = 0.00265$.

10.2.5 Let Y denote the distance between the pipeline and the point of impact. From Example 2.5.4, $P(A) = P(-20 \le Y \le 20) = \dfrac{10}{18}$. Let X_1 denote the number of missiles landing within 20 feet to the left of the pipeline, let X_2 denote the number of missiles landing within 20 feet to the right of the pipeline, and let X_3 denote the number of missiles for which $|y| > 20$. By the

symmetry of $f(y)$, $p_1 = P(-20 \le Y \le 0) = \dfrac{5}{18} = P(0 \le Y \le 20) = p_2$ (so $p_3 = P(|Y| > 20) = 1 -$

$\dfrac{5}{18} - \dfrac{5}{18} = \dfrac{8}{18}$). Therefore, $P(X_1 = 2, X_2 = 4, X_3 = 0) = \dfrac{6!}{2!4!0!}\left(\dfrac{5}{18}\right)^2\left(\dfrac{5}{18}\right)^4\left(\dfrac{8}{18}\right)^0 = 0.00649$.

10.2.7 a) $p_1 = P\left(0 \le Y < \dfrac{1}{4}\right) = \displaystyle\int_0^{1/4} 3y^2 dy = \dfrac{1}{64}$, $p_2 = P\left(\dfrac{1}{4} \le Y < \dfrac{1}{2}\right) = \displaystyle\int_{1/4}^{1/2} 3y^2 dy = \dfrac{7}{64}$,

$p_3 = P\left(\dfrac{1}{2} \le Y < \dfrac{3}{4}\right) = \displaystyle\int_{1/2}^{3/4} 3y^2 dy = \dfrac{19}{64}$, and $p_4 = P\left(\dfrac{3}{4} \le Y \le 1\right) = \displaystyle\int_{3/4}^{1} 3y^2 dy = \dfrac{37}{64}$.

Then $f_{X_1,X_2,X_3,X_4}(3,7,15,25) = P(X_1 = 3, X_2 = 7, X_3 = 15, X_4 = 25) =$

$\dfrac{50!}{3!7!15!25!}\left(\dfrac{1}{64}\right)^3\left(\dfrac{7}{64}\right)^7\left(\dfrac{19}{64}\right)^{15}\left(\dfrac{37}{64}\right)^{25}$.

b) By Theorem 10.2.2, X_3 is a binomial random variable with parameters n ($= 50$) and

$p_3 \left(= \dfrac{19}{64}\right)$. Therefore, $\text{Var}(X_3) = np_3(1 - p_3) = 50\left(\dfrac{19}{64}\right)\left(\dfrac{45}{64}\right) = 10.44$.

10.2.9 Assume that $M_{X_1X_2X_3}(t_1,t_2,t_3) = \left(p_1e^{t_1} + p_2e^{t_2} + p_3e^{t_3}\right)^n$. Then $M_{X_1,X_2,X_3}(t_1,0,0) =$

$E(e^{t_1X_1}) = \left(p_1e^{t_1} + p_2 + p_3\right)^n = (1 - p_1 + p_1e^{t_1})^n$ is the mgf for X_1. But the latter has the form of the mgf for a binomial random variable with parameters n and p_1.

Section 10.3

10.3.1 $\sum_{i=1}^{k}\frac{(X_i-np_i)^2}{np_i}=\sum_{i=1}^{k}\frac{(X_i^2-2np_iX_i+n^2p_i^2)}{np_i}=\sum_{i=1}^{k}\frac{X_i^2}{np_i}-2\sum_{i=1}^{k}X_i+n\sum_{i=1}^{k}p_i=\sum_{i=1}^{k}\frac{X_i^2}{np_i}-n.$

10.3.3 If the sampling is presumed to be <u>with</u> replacement, the number of white chips selected would follow a binomial distribution. Specifically, $\pi_1 = P(0$ whites are drawn$) =$

$\binom{2}{0}\left(\frac{4}{10}\right)^0\left(\frac{6}{10}\right)^2 = 0.36$, $\pi_2 = P(1$ white is drawn$) = \binom{2}{1}\left(\frac{4}{10}\right)^1\left(\frac{6}{10}\right)^1 = 0.48$, and

$\pi_3 = P(2$ whites are drawn$) = \binom{2}{2}\left(\frac{4}{10}\right)^2\left(\frac{6}{10}\right)^0 = 0.16$. The form of the $\alpha = 0.10$ decision rule

would be the same as in Question 10.3.2—reject H_0 if $c \ge \chi^2_{.90,2} = 4.605$. In this case,

though, $c = \dfrac{(35-100(0.36))^2}{100(0.36)} + \dfrac{(55-100(0.48))^2}{100(0.48)} + \dfrac{(10-100(0.16))^2}{100(0.16)} = 3.30$. Although

the binomial fit is not as good as the hypergeometric fit done in Question 10.3.2, the null hypothesis that the sampling occurred with replacement is not rejected.

10.3.5 Let $p = P($baby is born between midnight and 4 A.M.$)$. Test H_0: $p = \dfrac{1}{6}$ versus H_1: $p \ne \dfrac{1}{6}$.

Let $n =$ number of births $= 2650$ and $X =$ number of babies born between midnight and 4 A.M. $= 494$. From Theorem 6.3.1, H_0 should be rejected if z is either **1)** ≤ -1.96 or

2) $\ge 1.96 (= \pm z_{.025})$. Here $z = \dfrac{494 - 2650(1/6)}{\sqrt{2650(1/6)(5/6)}} = 2.73$, so H_0 is rejected. These two test

procedures are equivalent: If one rejects H_0, so will the other. Notice that $z^2_{.025} = (1.96)^2 = 3.84 = \chi^2_{.95,1}$ and (except for a small rounding error) $z^2 = \chi^2((2.73)^2 = 7.45 \doteq \chi^2 = 7.44)$.

10.3.7 Listed in the accompanying table are the observed and expected numbers of M&Ms of each color. Let $p_1 =$ true proportion of browns, $p_2 =$ true proportion of yellows, and so on.

Color	X_i	π_i	$E(X_i) = 1527 \cdot \pi_i$
Brown	455	0.30	458.1
Yellow	343	0.20	305.4
Red	318	0.20	305.4
Orange	152	0.10	152.7
Blue	130	0.10	152.7
Green	129	0.10	152.7
	1527	1	1527

To test H_0: $p_1 = 0.30, p_2 = 0.20, \ldots, p_6 = 0.10$ versus H_1: at least one $p_i \ne \pi_i$, reject H_0 if

$c \ge \chi^2_{.95,5} = 11.070$. But $c = \dfrac{(455-458.1)^2}{458.1} + \ldots + \dfrac{(129-152.7)^2}{152.7} = 12.23$, so H_0 is rejected

(these particular observed frequencies are not consistent with the company's intended probabilities).

10.3.9 Let the random variable X denote the length of a World Series. Then $P(X=4) = \pi_1 = P(\text{AL}$ wins in 4) + P(\text{NL wins in 4}) = 2 \cdot P(\text{AL wins in 4}) = 2\left(\dfrac{1}{2}\right)^4 = \dfrac{1}{8}$. Similarly, $P(X=5) = \pi_2 = 2 \cdot P(\text{AL wins in 5}) = 2 \cdot P(\text{Al wins exactly 3 of first 4 games}) \cdot P(\text{AL wins 5th game}) = 2 \cdot \binom{4}{3}\left(\dfrac{1}{2}\right)^3\left(\dfrac{1}{2}\right)^1 \cdot \dfrac{1}{2} = \dfrac{1}{4}$. Also, $P(X=6) = \pi_3 = 2 \cdot P(\text{AL wins exactly 3 of first 5 games}) \cdot P(\text{AL wins 6th game}) = 2 \cdot \binom{5}{3}\left(\dfrac{1}{2}\right)^3\left(\dfrac{1}{2}\right)^2 \cdot \left(\dfrac{1}{2}\right) = \dfrac{5}{16}$, and $P(X=7) = \pi_4 = 1 - P(X=4) - P(X=5) - P(X=6) = \dfrac{5}{16}$. Listed in the table is the information necessary for calculating the goodness-of-fit statistic c. The "Bernoulli model" is rejected if $c \geq \chi^2_{.90,3} = 6.251$. For these data, $c = \dfrac{(9-6.25)^2}{6.25} + \dfrac{(11-12.50)^2}{12.50} + \dfrac{(8-15.625)^2}{15.625} + \dfrac{(22-15.625)^2}{15.625} = 7.71$, so H_0 is rejected.

Number of games	Number of years	$50 \cdot \pi_i$
4	9	6.25
5	11	12.50
6	8	15.625
7	22	15.625
	50	50

10.3.11 Listed is the frequency distribution for the 70 y_i's using classes of width 10 starting at 220. If normality holds, each π_i is an integral of the normal pdf having $\mu = 266$ and $\sigma = 16$.

Duration, y	Freq.	π_i	$E(X_i)$	
$220 \leq y < 230$	1	0.0122	0.854	
$230 \leq y < 240$	5	0.0394	2.758	} 11.109
$240 \leq y < 250$	10	0.1071	7.497	
$250 \leq y < 260$	16	0.1933	13.531	
$260 \leq y < 270$	23	0.2467	17.269	
$270 \leq y < 280$	7	0.2119	14.833	
$280 \leq y < 290$	6	0.1226	8.582	} 13.258
$290 \leq y < 300$	2	0.0668	4.676	
	70	1	70	

For example, $\pi_2 = P(230 \leq Y < 240) = P\left(\dfrac{230-266}{16} \leq \dfrac{Y-266}{16} < \dfrac{240-266}{16}\right) = P(-2.25 \leq Z < -1.63) = 0.0394$. (Note: To account for all the area under $f_Y(y)$, the intervals defining the first and last classes need to be extended to $-\infty$ and $+\infty$, respectively. That is, $\pi_1 = P(-\infty < Y < 230)$ and $\pi_8 = P(290 \leq Y < \infty)$.) Some of the expected frequencies $(= 70 \cdot \pi_i)$ are too small (i.e., less than 5) for the χ^2 approximation to be fully adequate, so the first three classes need to be combined, as do the last two. With $k = 5$ final classes, then, the normality assumption is rejected if $c \geq \chi^2_{.90,4} = 7.779$. Here, $c =$

$$\frac{(16-11.109)^2}{11.109} + ... + \frac{(8-13.258)^2}{13.258} = 10.73,$$ so we would reject the null hypothesis that pregnancy durations are normally distributed.

Section 10.4

10.4.1 Let $p = P$(voter says "yes"). Then $\hat{p} = \dfrac{\text{number of yeses}}{\text{number of voters}} = \dfrac{30(0)+56(1)+73(2)+41(3)}{600} =$

0.54, so the H_0 model to be tested is $P(k \text{ yeses}) = \begin{pmatrix} 3 \\ k \end{pmatrix}(0.54)^k(0.46)^{3-k}$, $k = 0, 1, 2, 3$.

Detailed in the accompanying table are the relevant observed and expected frequencies. At the $\alpha = 0.05$ level, the binomial model should be rejected if $c_1 \geq \chi^2_{.95,4-1-1} = 5.991$.

No. saying "yes"	Freq.	$\hat{p}_i$	$200 \cdot \hat{p}_i$
0	30	0.097	19.4
1	56	0.343	68.6
2	73	0.402	80.4
3	41	0.157	31.4
	200	1.00	200

But $c_1 = \dfrac{(30-19.4)^2}{19.4} + \dfrac{(56-68.6)^2}{68.6} + \dfrac{(73-80.4)^2}{80.4} + \dfrac{(41-31.4)^2}{31.4} = 11.72$, implying that the binomial model is inadequate in this particular context (probably because the trials are not likely to be independent, which is one of the model's assumptions).

10.4.3 Here the H_0 model is $P(y \text{ infected plants}) = e^{-\hat{\lambda}}(\hat{\lambda})^y / y!$, $y = 0, 1, 2, ...$, where $\hat{\lambda} = \bar{y} = \dfrac{38(0)+57(1)+...+1(12)}{270} = 2.53$. As the table clearly shows, the Poisson model is inappropriate for these data. The disagreements between the observed and expected frequencies are considerable—$c_1 = \dfrac{(38-21.52)^2}{21.52} + ... + \dfrac{(28-11.88)^2}{11.88} = 46.75$, which greatly exceeds the $\alpha = 0.05$ critical value, $\chi^2_{.95,7-1-1} = 11.070$. The independence assumption would not hold if the infestation was contagious (which is likely to be the case).

No. of Infected Plants	No. of Quadrats	$\hat{p}_i$	$270 \cdot \hat{p}_i$
0	38	0.0797	21.52
1	57	0.2015	54.41
2	68	0.2549	68.82
3	47	0.2150	58.05
4	23	0.1360	36.72
5	9	0.0688	18.58
6	10	0.0290	7.83
7	7	0.0105	2.84
8	3	0.0033	0.89
9	4	0.0009	0.24
10	2	0.0002	0.05
11	1	0.0001	0.03
12	1	0.0000	0.00
13+	0	0.0000	0.00
	270	1.00	270.0

(Values for 6 through 13+ bracketed together: 11.88)

10.4.5 Under H_0, the intervals between shutdowns should be described by an exponential pdf, $f_Y(y) = \hat{\lambda}e^{-\hat{\lambda}y}, y > 0$, where $\hat{\lambda} = 1/\bar{y}$ (recall Theorem 4.2.3). Here, the sample mean can be approximated by assigning each observation in a range a value equal to the midpoint of that range. Therefore, $\bar{y} \doteq \dfrac{130(0.5) + 41(1.5) + \ldots + 1(7.5)}{211} = 1.22$, which makes $\hat{\lambda} = 0.82$.

Moreover, each $\hat{p}_i$ is an area under $f_Y(y)$. For example, $\hat{p}_1 = \int_0^1 0.82e^{-0.82y}dy = 0.56$. The complete set of $\hat{p}_i$'s and estimated expected frequencies are listed in the accompanying table. Using $k = 5$ final classes, we should reject the exponential model if $c_1 \geq \chi^2_{.95,5-1-1} = 7.815$. But $c_1 = \dfrac{(130-118.16)^2}{118.16} + \ldots + \dfrac{(7-8.01)^2}{8.01} = 4.2$, so H_0 is not rejected.

Interval	Freq.	$\hat{p}_i$	$211 \cdot \hat{p}_i$
$0 \leq y < 1$	130	0.560	118.16
$1 \leq y < 2$	41	0.246	51.91
$2 \leq y < 3$	25	0.109	23.00
$3 \leq y < 4$	8	0.047	9.92
$4 \leq y < 5$	2	0.021	4.43
$5 \leq y < 6$	3	0.010	2.11
$6 \leq y < 7$	1	0.004	0.84
$y \geq 7$	1	0.003	0.63
	211	1	211

(Values for $4 \leq y < 5$ through $y \geq 7$ bracketed together: 8.01)

10.4.7 If $p = P$(child is a boy), $\hat{p} = \dfrac{\text{number of boys}}{\text{number of children}} = \dfrac{24(0) + 64(1) + 32(2)}{240} = 0.533$, so the

hypotheses to be tested are H_0: $P(k \text{ boys}) = \binom{2}{k}(0.533)^k(0.467)^{2-k}$, $k = 0, 1, 2$, versus H_1:

$P(k \text{ boys}) \neq \binom{2}{k}(0.533)^k(0.467)^{2-k}$, $k = 0, 1, 2$. Summarized in the table are the observed

and expected numbers of families with 0, 1, and 2 boys. Given that k = number of classes = 3

and that 1 parameter has been estimated, H_0 should be rejected if $c_1 \geq \chi^2_{.95,3-1-1} = 3.841$. But

$c_1 = \dfrac{(24 - 26.2)^2}{26.2} + \dfrac{(64 - 59.7)^2}{59.7} + \dfrac{(32 - 34.1)^2}{34.1} = 0.62$, implying that the binomial model

should not be rejected.

No. of boys	Freq.	$\hat{p}_i$	$120 \cdot \hat{p}_i$
0	24	0.2181	26.2
1	64	0.4978	59.7
2	32	0.2841	34.1
	120	1	120

10.4.9 Given that $\hat{\lambda} = 3.87$, the model to fit under H_0 is $p_X(k) = e^{-3.87}(3.87)^k/k!$, $k = 0, 1, 2, \ldots$
Multiplying the latter probabilities by 2608 gives the complete set of estimated expected
frequencies, as shown in the table. No classes need to be combined, so $k = 12$ and one

parameter has been estimated. Let $\alpha = 0.05$. Then H_0 should be rejected if $c_1 \geq \chi^2_{.95,12-1-1} =$

18.307. But $\dfrac{(57 - 54.51)^2}{54.51} + \dfrac{(203 - 210.47)^2}{210.47} + \ldots + \dfrac{(6 - 6.00)^2}{6.00} = 12.92$, implying that the

Poisson model should not be rejected.

No. detected, k	Freq.	$\hat{p}_i (= p_X(k))$	$2608 \cdot \hat{p}_i$
0	57	0.0209	54.51
1	203	0.0807	210.47
2	383	0.1562	407.37
3	525	0.2015	525.51
4	532	0.1949	508.30
5	408	0.1509	393.55
6	273	0.0973	253.76
7	139	0.0538	140.31
8	45	0.0260	67.81
9	27	0.0112	29.21
10	10	0.0043	11.21
11+	6	0.0023	6.00
	2608	1	2608.0

10.4.11 From Example 5.2.1, the MLE for p is the reciprocal of the sample mean. Here,

$$\hat{p} = \frac{50}{4(1) + 13(2) + ... + 1(9)} = 0.26, \text{ so the } H_0 \text{ model becomes } p_X(k) = (1 - 0.26)^{k-1}(0.26),$$

$k = 1, 2, ...$ Combining the last five classes (see the accompanying table) makes $k = 5$. Let $\alpha = 0.05$. Then H_0 should be rejected if $c_1 \geq \chi^2_{.95, 5-1-1} = 7.815$. In this case, $c_2 =$

$$\frac{(4-13.00)^2}{13.00} + \frac{(13-9.62)^2}{9.62} + ... + \frac{(16-15.00)^2}{15.00} = 9.23, \text{ which suggests that the 50}$$

observations did not come from a geometric pdf.

Outcome	Freq.	$\hat{p}_i \; (= p_X(k))$	$50 \cdot \hat{p}_i$	
1	4	0.2600	13.00	
2	13	0.1924	9.62	
3	10	0.1424	7.12	
4	7	0.1054	5.27	
5	5	0.0780	3.90	
6	4	0.0577	2.89	
7	3	0.0427	2.14	15.00
8	3	0.0316	1.58	
9+	1	0.0898	4.49	
	50	1	50.0	

Section 10.5

10.5.1 To test H_0: Telephone listing and home ownership are independent at the $\alpha = 0.05$ level, reject H_0 if $c_2 \geq \chi^2_{.95, (2-1)(2-1)} = 3.841$. If α is increased to 0.10, the critical value reduces to $\chi^2_{.90,1} = 2.706$. Based on the expected frequencies predicted by H_0 (see the accompanying table), $c_2 = 2.77$ so H_0 is rejected at the $\alpha = 0.10$ level, but not at the $\alpha = 0.05$ level.

	Listed	Unlisted	
Own	628	146	774
	(619.20)	(154.80)	
Rent	172	54	226
	(180.80)	(45.20)	
	800	200	1000

10.5.3 To test H_0: Delinquency and birth order are independent versus H_1: Delinquency and birth order are dependent at the $\alpha = 0.01$ level, reject the null hypothesis if $c_2 \geq \chi^2_{.99,(4-1)(2-1)} =$ 11.345. Here, $c_2 = \dfrac{(24-45.59)^2}{45.59} + ... + \dfrac{(70-84.05)^2}{84.05} = 42.25$, suggesting that delinquency and birth order <u>are</u> related.

	Delinquent	Not delinquent	
<u>Oldest</u>	24	450	474
	(45.59)	(428.41)	
<u>In between</u>	29	312	341
	(32.80)	(308.20)	
<u>Youngest</u>	35	211	246
	(23.66)	(222.34)	
<u>Only</u>	23	70	93
	(8.95)	(84.05)	
	111	1043	1154

10.5.5 The null hypothesis that adults' self-perception and attitude toward small cars are independent should be rejected at the $\alpha = 0.01$ level if $c_2 \geq \chi^2_{.99,(3-1)(3-1)} = 13.277$. These data suggest that the two are <u>not</u> independent (and H_0 should be rejected)—$c_2 = \dfrac{(79-61.59)^2}{61.59} + ... + \dfrac{(42-28.76)^2}{28.76} = 27.29$.

	Cautious	Middle	Confident	
<u>Favorable</u>	79	58	49	186
	(61.59)	(62.21)	(62.21)	
<u>Neutral</u>	10	8	9	27
	(8.94)	(9.03)	(9.03)	
<u>Unfavorable</u>	10	34	42	86
	(28.47)	(28.76)	(28.76)	
	99	100	100	299

10.5.7 Given that $\alpha = 0.05$, the null hypothesis that early upbringing and aggressiveness later in life are independent is rejected if $c_2 \geq \chi^2_{.95,(2-1)(2-1)} = 3.841$. But $c_2 = \dfrac{(27-40.25)^2}{40.25} + ... + \dfrac{(93-106.25)^2}{106.25} = 12.61$, so H_0 <u>is</u> rejected—mice raised by foster mothers appear to be more aggressive than mice raised by their natural mothers.

	Natural mother	Foster mother	
<u>No. fighting</u>	27	47	74
	(40.25)	(33.75)	
<u>No. not fighting</u>	140	93	233
	(126.75)	(106.25)	
	167	140	307

10.5.9 Let $\alpha = 0.05$. To test the null hypothesis that annual return and portfolio turnover are independent, we should reject H_0 if $c_2 \geq \chi^2_{.95,(2-1)(2-1)} = 3.841$. Based on the table below, the value of c_2 in this case is $2.20 \left(= \dfrac{(11-13.86)^2}{13.86} + ... + \dfrac{(24-26.86)^2}{26.86} \right)$, so the appropriate conclusion would be that annual return and portfolio turnover <u>are</u> independent.

		Annual return		
		$\leq 10\%$	$> 10\%$	
<u>Portfolio</u>	$\geq 100\%$	11	10	21
<u>return</u>		(13.86)	(7.14)	
	$<100\%$	55	24	79
		(52.14)	(26.86)	
		66	34	100

Chapter 11

Section 11.2

11.2.1 $\beta_1 = \dfrac{n\sum\limits_{i=1}^{n}x_iy_i - \left(\sum\limits_{i=1}^{n}x_i\right)\left(\sum\limits_{i=1}^{n}y_i\right)}{n\left(\sum\limits_{i=1}^{n}x_i^2\right) - \left(\sum\limits_{i=1}^{n}x_i\right)^2} = \dfrac{15(20{,}127.47) - (249.8)(1{,}200.6)}{15(4200.56) - (249.8)^2} = 3.291$

$\beta_0 = \dfrac{\sum\limits_{i=1}^{n}y_i - \beta_1\sum\limits_{i=1}^{n}x_i}{n} = \dfrac{1{,}200.6 - 3.291(249.8)}{15} = 25.234$

Then $y = 25.234 + 3.291x$; $y(18) = 84.5°F$

11.2.3 $\beta_1 = \dfrac{n\sum\limits_{i=1}^{n}x_iy_i - \left(\sum\limits_{i=1}^{n}x_i\right)\left(\sum\limits_{i=1}^{n}y_i\right)}{n\left(\sum\limits_{i=1}^{n}x_i^2\right) - \left(\sum\limits_{i=1}^{n}x_i\right)^2} = \dfrac{9(24{,}628.6) - (234)(811.3)}{9(10{,}144) - (234)^2} = 0.8706$

$\beta_0 = \dfrac{\sum\limits_{i=1}^{n}y_i - \beta_1\sum\limits_{i=1}^{n}x_i}{n} = \dfrac{811.3 - 0.8706(234)}{9} = 67.5088$

As an example of calculating a residual, consider $x_2 = 4$. Then the corresponding residual is $y_2 - \hat{y}_2 = 71.0 - [67.5088 + 0.8706(4)] = 0.0098$. The complete set of residuals, rounded to two decimal places is

x_i	$y_i - \hat{y}_i$
0	−0.81
4	0.01
10	0.09
15	0.03
21	−0.09
29	0.14
36	0.55
51	1.69
68	−1.61

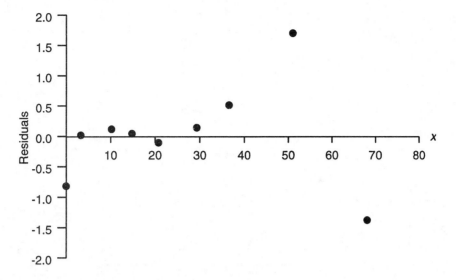

A straight line appears to fit these data.

11.2.5 The value 12 is too "far" from the data observed.

11.2.7 $\beta_1 = \dfrac{13(48,593,986) - (54,975)(11,431)}{13(237,083,328) - (54,975)^2} = 0.0552$

$\beta_0 = \dfrac{11,431 - 0.0552(54,975)}{13} = 645.88$

The least squares line is $645.88 + 0.0552x$. The residuals sorted by the size of the x values are:

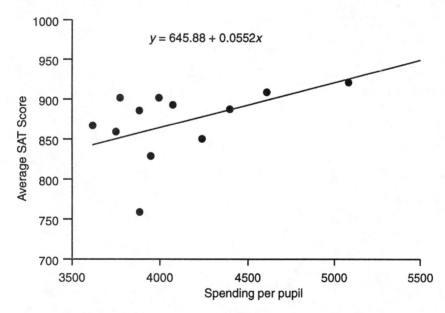

The linear fit for x values less than \$4300 is not very good, suggesting a search for other contributing variables in the x range of \$3500 to \$4200.

11.2.9 $\beta_1 = \dfrac{9(7,439.37) - (41.56)(1,416.1)}{9(289.4222) - (41.56)^2} = 9.23$

$\beta_0 = \dfrac{(1,416.1) - 9.23(41.56)}{9} = 114.72$

A linear relationship seems reasonable.

11.2.11 $\beta_1 = \dfrac{11(1141) - (111)(100)}{11(1277) - (111)^2} = 0.84$

$\beta_0 = \dfrac{1072 - 0.84(111)}{11} = 0.61$

The least squares line is $y = 0.61 + 0.84x$. The residuals given in the table below are large relative to the x values, which suggests that the linear fit is inadequate.

x_i	$y_i - \hat{y}_i$
7	−3.5
13	−1.5
14	−1.4
6	−0.7
14	2.6
15	1.8
4	3.0
8	2.7
7	−2.5
9	0.8
14	−1.4

11.2.13 When $\bar{x}$ is substituted for x in the least-squares line equation, we obtain

$$y = \beta_0 + \beta_1\bar{x} = \bar{y} - \beta_1\bar{x} + \beta_1\bar{x} = \bar{y}.$$

11.2.15 For these data $\sum_{i=1}^{n} d_iv_i = 95{,}161.2$, and $\sum_{i=1}^{n} d_i^2 = 2{,}685{,}141$.

Then $H = \dfrac{\sum_{i=1}^{n} d_iv_i}{\sum_{i=1}^{n} d_i^2} = \dfrac{95{,}161.2}{2{,}685{,}141} = 0.3544$.

11.2.17 $\beta_1 = \dfrac{\sum_{i=1}^{n} x_iy_i - \beta_0^*\sum_{i=1}^{n} x_i}{\sum_{i=1}^{n} x_i^2} = \dfrac{1513 - 100(45)}{575.5} = -5.19$, so $y = 100 - 5.19x$.

11.2.19 a)   One choice for the model is $y = \beta_0 e^{\beta_1 x}$. Then $\ln y$ is linear with x. Using Theorem 9.2.1 on the x_i and the $\ln y_i$ gives

$$\beta_1 = \dfrac{n\sum_{i=1}^{n} x_i \ln y_i - \left(\sum_{i=1}^{n} x_i\right)\left(\sum_{i=1}^{n} \ln y_i\right)}{n\left(\sum_{i=1}^{n} x_i^2\right) - \left(\sum_{i=1}^{n} x_i\right)^2}$$

$$= \dfrac{10\sum_{i=1}^{n} 137.97415 - (35)(41.35720)}{10(169) - 35^2} = -0.14572$$

$$\ln \beta_0 = \dfrac{\sum_{i=1}^{n} \ln y_i - \beta_1\sum_{i=1}^{n} x_i}{n}$$

$$= \dfrac{41.35720 - (-0.14572)(35)}{10} = 4.64574.$$ Then β_0 rounded to three decimal places is

$e^{4.64574} = 104.140$. The desired exponential fit is $y = 104.140e^{-0.146x}$. This model fits the data well. However, note that the initial percentage by this model is 104.141, when we know it must be 100. This discrepancy suggests using Question 11.2.16 where $\beta_0^* = 100$. In this case,

$$\beta_1 = \dfrac{\sum_{i=1}^{n} x_i \ln y_i - \ln \beta_0^*\left(\sum_{i=1}^{n} x_i\right)}{\sum_{i=1}^{n} x_i^2} = \dfrac{137.97415 - 4.60517(35)}{169} = -0.13732.$$

This model is $y = 100e^{-0.137x}$.

b)   For the first model, the half life is the solution to $50 = 104.140e^{-0.146x}$, or $\ln(50/104.140) = -0.146x$, so $x = 5.025$.
For the second model, the half life is the solution to $0.5 = e^{-0.137x}$ or $\ln 0.5 = -0.137x$, so $x = 5.059$.

11.2.21 a) $\beta_1 = \dfrac{6(175.38297) - (21)(50.90618)}{6(91) - 21^2} = -0.15935$

$\ln \beta_0 = \dfrac{\displaystyle\sum_{i=1}^{n} \ln y_i - \beta_1 \sum_{i=1}^{n} x_i}{n} = \dfrac{50.90618 - (-0.15935)(21)}{6} = 9.04209$

Then $\beta_0 = e^{9.0409} = 8451.4$, and the model is $y = 8451.4e^{-0.159x}$

b) $y(7) = 8451.4e^{-0.159(7)} = \$2777$

c)   The exponential curve, which fits the data very well, predicts that a car 0 years old will have a value of \$8451, significantly less than the selling price of \$9630.

11.2.23 a)   If $\dfrac{dy}{dx} = \beta_1 y$, then $\dfrac{1}{y}\dfrac{dy}{dx} = \beta_1$.   Integrate both sides of the latter equality with respect to x:

$\displaystyle\int \dfrac{1}{y}\dfrac{dy}{dx}\, dx = \int \beta_1 dx$, which implies that $\ln y = \beta_1 x + C$.

Now apply the function e^x to both sides to get

$y = e^{\beta_1 x}e^c = \beta_0 e^{\beta_1 x}$, where $\beta_0 = e^c$.

b) x on the abscissa, $\ln y$ on the ordinate

11.2.25 a) $\beta_1 = \dfrac{n\displaystyle\sum_{i=1}^{n} \log x_i \cdot \log y - \left(\sum_{i=1}^{n}\log x_i\right)\left(\sum_{i=1}^{n}\log y_i\right)}{n\left(\displaystyle\sum_{i=1}^{n}\log^2 x_i\right) - \left(\sum_{i=1}^{n}\log x_i\right)^2}$

$= \dfrac{15(156.03811) - (41.77441)(52.79857)}{15(126.6045) - 41.77441^2} = 0.87644$

$\log \beta_0 = \dfrac{\displaystyle\sum_{i=1}^{n}\log y_i - \beta_1\left(\sum_{i=1}^{n}\log x_i\right)}{n} = \dfrac{52.79857 - 0.87644(41.77441)}{15} = 1.07905$

$\beta_0 = 11.99637$, and the model is $y = 11.99637x^{0.87644}$

b) $y(2500) = 11.99637(2500)^{0.87644} = 11{,}406$

11.2.27 $\beta_1 = \dfrac{n\sum\limits_{i=1}^{n}(1/x_i)y_i - \left(\sum\limits_{i=1}^{n}1/x_i\right)\left(\sum\limits_{i=1}^{n}y_i\right)}{n\left(\sum\limits_{i=1}^{n}(1/x_i)^2\right) - \left(\sum\limits_{i=1}^{n}1/x_i\right)^2} = \dfrac{7(435.625) - (8.01667)(169.1)}{7(21.35028) - 8.01667^2} = 19.82681$

$\beta_0 = \dfrac{\sum\limits_{i=1}^{n}y_i - \beta_1\left(\sum\limits_{i=1}^{n}1/x_i\right)}{n} = \dfrac{169.7 - 19.82681(8.01667)}{7} = 1.53643$

One quarter mile = 0.25(5,280) = 1,320 feet.

$y(1.32) = 1.53643 + (19.82681)(1/1.32) = 16.557$, or \$16,557

11.2.29 Let $y' = \ln\left(\dfrac{1055 - y}{y}\right)$. We find the linear relationship between x and y'. The needed sums

are $\sum\limits_{i=1}^{10}x_i = 55,\ \sum\limits_{i=1}^{10}x_i^2 = 385,\ \sum\limits_{i=1}^{10}y_i' = -17.28636,\ \sum\limits_{i=1}^{10}x_iy_i' = -201.76600.$

$\beta_1 = \dfrac{10(-201.76600) - 55(-17.28636)}{10(385) - 55^2} = -1.29322$

$\beta_0 = \dfrac{-17.28636 - (-1.29322)(55)}{10} = 5.38407$

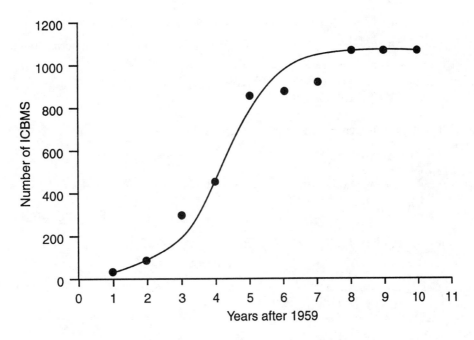

Section 11.3

11.3.1 $\beta_1 = \dfrac{4(93) - 10(40.2)}{4(30) - 10^2} = -1.5$

$\beta_0 = \dfrac{(40.2) - (-1.5)(10)}{4} = 13.8$

Thus, $y = 13.8 - 1.5x$. $t = \dfrac{\hat{\beta}_1 - \beta_1^0}{s / \sqrt{\sum\limits_{i=1}^{4}(x_i - \bar{x})^2}} = \dfrac{-1.5 - 0}{2.114 / \sqrt{5}} = -1.59$

Since $-t_{0.025,2} = -4.3027 < t = -1.59 < 4.3027 = t_{0.025,2}$, accept H_0.

11.3.3 $t = \dfrac{\beta_1 - \beta_1^0}{s / \sqrt{\sum\limits_{i=1}^{15}(x_i - \bar{x})^2}} = \dfrac{3.291 - 0}{3.829 / \sqrt{40.55733}} = 5.47.$

Since $t = 5.47 > t_{0.005,13} = 3.0123$, reject H_0.

11.3.5 $\text{Var}(\hat{\beta}_1) = \sigma^2 / \sum\limits_{i=1}^{9}(x_i - \bar{x})^2 = 45/60 = 0.75$. The standard deviation of $\hat{\beta}_1 = \sqrt{0.75} = 0.866$.

$P\left(\left|\hat{\beta}_1 - \beta_1\right| < 1.5\right) = P\left(\dfrac{\left|\hat{\beta}_1 - \beta_1\right|}{0.866} < \dfrac{1.5}{0.866}\right) = P(|Z| < 1.73)$ for the standard normal random

variable Z. $P(Z > 1.73) = 1 - 0.9582 = 0.0418$,
so $P(|Z| < 1.73) = 1 - 2(0.0418) = 0.9164$

11.3.7 The radius of the confidence interval is

$t_{0.05,7} \dfrac{s\sqrt{\sum\limits_{i=1}^{n} x_i^2}}{\sqrt{7}\sqrt{\sum\limits_{i=1}^{n}(x_i - \bar{x})^2}} = 1.8946 \dfrac{(0.959)\sqrt{10144}}{\sqrt{7}\sqrt{4060}} = 0.958$

The center of the interval is $\hat{\beta}_0 = 67.508$. The interval = $(66.550, 68.466)$

11.3.9 $t = \dfrac{\hat{\beta}_1 - \beta_1^0}{s / \sqrt{\sum\limits_{i=1}^{11}(x_i - \bar{x})^2}} = \dfrac{0.84 - 0}{2.404 / \sqrt{156.909}} = 4.38$

Since $t = 4.38 > t_{0.025,9} = 2.2622$, reject H_0.

11.3.11 By Theorem 11.3.2, $E(\hat{\beta}_0) = \beta_0$, and $\text{Var}(\hat{\beta}_0) = \dfrac{\sigma^2 \sum\limits_{i=1}^{n} x_i}{n \sum\limits_{i=1}^{n}(x_i - \bar{x})^2}$.

Now, $(\hat{\beta}_0 - \beta_0)/\sqrt{\text{Var}(\hat{\beta}_0)}$ is normal, so $P\left(-z_{\alpha/2} < (\hat{\beta}_0 - \beta_0)/\sqrt{\text{Var}(\hat{\beta}_0)} < z_{\alpha/2}\right) = 1 - \alpha$.

Then the confidence interval is

$(\hat{\beta}_0 - z_{\alpha/2}\sqrt{\text{Var}(\hat{\beta}_0)}, \ \hat{\beta}_0 + z_{\alpha/2}\sqrt{\text{Var}(\hat{\beta}_0)})$ or

$$\left(\hat{\beta}_0 - z_{\alpha/2} \frac{\sigma\sqrt{\sum\limits_{i=1}^{n} x_i}}{\sqrt{n}\sqrt{\sum\limits_{i=1}^{n}(x_i - \bar{x})^2}}, \ \hat{\beta}_0 + z_{\alpha/2} \frac{\sigma\sqrt{\sum\limits_{i=1}^{n} x_i}}{\sqrt{n}\sqrt{\sum\limits_{i=1}^{n}(x_i - \bar{x})^2}} \right)$$

11.3.13 From Theorem 11.3.3, we know that

$$P\left(\chi^2_{\alpha/2,n-2} < \frac{n\hat{\sigma}^2}{\sigma^2} < \chi^2_{1-\alpha/2,n-2} \right) = 1 - \alpha. \text{ Interverting the inequality gives}$$

$$P\left(\frac{1}{\chi^2_{1-\alpha/2,n-2}} < \frac{\sigma^2}{n\hat{\sigma}^2} < \frac{1}{\chi^2_{\alpha/2,n-2}} \right) = 1 - \alpha \text{ or } P\left(\frac{n\hat{\sigma}^2}{\chi^2_{1-\alpha/2,n-2}} < \sigma^2 < \frac{n\hat{\sigma}^2}{\chi^2_{\alpha/2,n-2}} \right) = 1 - \alpha. \text{ Since}$$

$s^2 = \dfrac{n}{n-2}\hat{\sigma}^2$, $(n-2)s^2 = n\hat{\sigma}^2$. Thus, the desired confidence interval is

$$\left(\frac{(n-2)s^2}{\chi^2_{1-\alpha/2,n-2}}, \frac{(n-2)s^2}{\chi^2_{\alpha/2,n-2}} \right).$$

11.3.15 a) The test statistic for β_0 is

$$t = \frac{(\hat{\beta}_0 - \beta_0^o)\sqrt{n}\sqrt{\sum\limits_{i=1}^{n}(x_i - \bar{x})^2}}{s\sqrt{x_i^2}} = \frac{(-0.2281-0)\sqrt{10}\sqrt{1568.625}}{0.2067\sqrt{6974.25}} = -1.65$$

Since $-t_{0.025,8} = -2.3060 < t = -1.65 < 2.3060 = t_{0.025,8}$, accept H_0.

b) To test β_1 use $\dfrac{\hat{\beta}_1 - \beta_1^0}{s/\sqrt{\sum\limits_{i=1}^{11}(x_i - \bar{x})^2}} = \dfrac{0.9948-1}{0.2067/\sqrt{1568.625}} = -1.00.$

Since $-t_{0.025,8} = -2.3060 < t = -1.00 < 2.3060 = t_{0.025,8}$, accept H_0.

11.3.17 The radius of the 95% confidence interval is

$$2.0687(0.0113)\sqrt{\frac{1}{25} + \frac{(2.750-2.643)^2}{0.0367}} = 0.0139$$

The center is $\hat{y} = \hat{\beta}_0 + \hat{\beta}_1 x = 0.308 + 0.642(2.750) = 2.0735.$ The confidence interval is (2.0596, 2.0874)

11.3.19 The radius of the 95% prediction interval is $2.7764(6.987)\sqrt{1+\dfrac{1}{6}+\dfrac{(7-3.5)^2}{17.5}} = 26.504.$

The center is $\hat{y} = \hat{\beta}_0 + \hat{\beta}_1 x = 97.867 - 11.057(7) = 20.468.$

The 95% prediction interval for 1996 ($x = 7$) is $(-6.04, 46.97)$ so the worst-case scenario is 47 near-collisions.

11.3.21 The test statistic is $t = \dfrac{\hat{\beta}_1 - \hat{\beta}_1^*}{s\sqrt{\dfrac{1}{\sum\limits_{i=1}^{10}(x_i - \bar{x})^2} + \dfrac{1}{\sum\limits_{i=1}^{10}(x_i^* - \bar{x}^*)^2}}}$, where

$s = \sqrt{\dfrac{1}{8+8}(8s^2 + 8s*^2)} = \sqrt{\dfrac{1}{2}(0.2067^2 + 0.1261^2)} = 0.1712.$

Then $t = \dfrac{0.9948 - 1.0024}{0.1712\sqrt{\dfrac{1}{1568.625} + \dfrac{1}{1568.625}}} = -1.24$

Since $-t_{0.025,16} = -2.1199 < t = -1.24 < 2.1199 = t_{0.025,16}$, accept H_0. There is no statistical basis for preferring one method over the other, so it would be reasonable to choose the second, less expensive, method.

11.3.23 $s = \sqrt{\dfrac{1}{3+4}(3s^2 + 4s*^2)} = \sqrt{\dfrac{1}{7}[3(0.9058^2) + 4(1.2368^2)]} = 1.1071.$

Then $t = \dfrac{-3.4615 + 2.7373}{1.1071\sqrt{\dfrac{1}{26} + \dfrac{1}{39.3333}}} = -2.59$

Since $t = -2.59 < -t_{0.025,7} = -2.3646$, reject H_0.

11.3.25 $\sum\limits_{i=1}^{n}(\hat{Y}_i - \bar{Y})^2 = \sum\limits_{i=1}^{n}(\hat{\beta}_0 + \hat{\beta}_1 x_i - \bar{Y})^2$

$= \sum\limits_{i=1}^{n}(\bar{Y} - \hat{\beta}_1\bar{x} + \hat{\beta}_1 x_i - \bar{Y})^2 = \sum\limits_{i=1}^{n}(\hat{\beta}_1 x_i - \hat{\beta}_1\bar{x})^2 = \hat{\beta}_1^2\sum\limits_{i=1}^{n}(x_i - \bar{x})^2$

An application of Equation 11.3.2 completes the proof.

Section 11.4

11.4.1

x	y	$f_{X,Y}$	xy	$xyf_{X,Y}$
1	1	1/36	1	1/36
1	2	1/36	2	2/36
1	3	1/36	3	3/36
1	4	1/36	4	4/36
1	5	1/36	5	5/36
1	6	1/36	6	6/36
2	2	2/36	4	8/36
2	3	1/36	6	6/36
2	4	1/36	8	8/36
2	5	1/36	10	10/36
2	6	1/36	12	12/36
3	3	3/36	9	27/36
3	4	1/36	12	12/36
3	5	1/36	15	15/36
3	6	1/36	18	18/36
4	4	4/36	16	64/36
4	5	1/36	20	20/36
4	6	1/36	24	24/36
5	5	5/36	25	125/36
5	6	1/36	30	30/36
6	6	6/36	36	216/36

$E(XY)$ is the sum of the last column $= \dfrac{616}{36}$

Clearly $E(X) = 7/2$.

$$E(Y) = 1\frac{1}{36} + 2\frac{2}{36} + 3\frac{5}{36} + 4\frac{7}{36} + 5\frac{9}{36} + 6\frac{11}{36} = \frac{161}{36}$$

$$\text{Cov}(X,Y) = E(XY) - E(X)E(Y) = \frac{616}{36} - \frac{7}{2}\cdot\frac{161}{36} = \frac{105}{72}$$

11.4.3 $\displaystyle\int_0^{2\pi} \cos x\,dx = \int_0^{2\pi} \sin x\,dx = \int_0^{2\pi} (\cos x)(\sin x)\,dx = 0$, so $E(X) = E(Y) = E(XY) = 0$.

Then $\text{Cov}(X, Y) = 0$. But X and Y are functionally dependent, $Y = \sqrt{1 - X^2}$, so they are probabilistically dependent.

11.4.5 $E(XY) = 1\dfrac{1 + 2(1)}{22} + 2\dfrac{2 + 2(1)}{22} + 3\dfrac{1 + 2(3)}{22} + 6\dfrac{2 + 2(3)}{22} = 80/22 = 40/11$

$E(X) = 1\dfrac{10}{22} + 2\dfrac{12}{22} = 34/22 = 17/11$

$E(X^2) = 1\dfrac{10}{22} + 4\dfrac{12}{22} = 58/22 = 29/11$

$E(Y) = 1\dfrac{7}{22} + 3\dfrac{15}{22} = 52/22 = 26/11$

$$E(Y^2) = 1\frac{7}{22} + 9\frac{15}{22} = 142/22 = 71/11$$

$$\text{Cov}(XY) = 40/11 - (17/11)(26/11) = -2/121$$

$$\text{Var}(X) = 29/11 - (17/11)^2 = 30/121$$

$$\text{Var}(Y) = 71/11 - (26/11)^2 = 105/121$$

$$\rho(X,Y) = \frac{-2/121}{\sqrt{30/121}\sqrt{105/121}} = \frac{-2}{\sqrt{3150}} = \frac{-2}{15\sqrt{14}} = 0.036$$

11.4.7 $E(X^2) = \int_0^1 x^2(4x^3)dx = 2/3.$ $\text{Var}(X) = 2/3 - (4/5)^2 = 2/75$

$E(Y^2) = \int_0^1 y^2(4y - 4y^3)dx = 1/3.$ $\text{Var}(Y) = 1/3 - (8/15)^2 = 11/225.$

$$\rho = \frac{8/450}{\sqrt{2/75}\sqrt{11/225}} = 0.492$$

11.4.9 $\rho(a + bX, c + dY) = \dfrac{\text{Cov}(a+bX, c+dY)}{\sqrt{\text{Var}(a+bX)\text{Var}(c+dY)}} = \dfrac{bd\text{Cov}(X,Y)}{\sqrt{b^2\text{Var}(X)d^2\text{Var}(Y)}}$, the equality in the

numerator stemming from Question 11.4.2. Since $b > 0$, $d > 0$, this last expression is
$$\frac{bd\text{Cov}(X,Y)}{bd\sigma_X\sigma_Y} = \frac{\text{Cov}(X,Y)}{\sigma_X\sigma_Y} = \rho(X,Y).$$

11.4.11 $\text{Cov}(X + Y, X - Y) = E[(X+Y)(X-Y)] - E(X+Y)E(X-Y)$
$= E[X^2 - Y^2] - (\mu_X + \mu_Y)(\mu_X - \mu_Y)$
$= E(X^2) - \mu_X - E(Y^2) + \mu_Y = \text{Var}(X) - \text{Var}(Y)$

11.4.13 Multiply the numerator and denominator of Equation 11.4.1 by n^2 to obtain

$$R = \frac{n\sum_{i=1}^{n}X_iY_i - \left(\sum_{i=1}^{n}X_i\right)\left(\sum_{i=1}^{n}Y_i\right)}{\sqrt{n\sum_{i=1}^{n}(X_i - \bar{X})^2}\sqrt{n\sum_{i=1}^{n}(Y_i - \bar{Y})^2}} = \frac{n\sum_{i=1}^{n}X_iY_i - \left(\sum_{i=1}^{n}X_i\right)\left(\sum_{i=1}^{n}Y_i\right)}{\sqrt{n\sum_{i=1}^{n}X_i^2 - \left(\sum_{i=1}^{n}X_i\right)^2}\sqrt{n\sum_{i=1}^{n}Y_i^2 - \left(\sum_{i=1}^{n}Y_i\right)^2}}$$

11.4.15 $r = \dfrac{n\sum_{i=1}^{n}x_iy_i - \left(\sum_{i=1}^{n}x_i\right)\left(\sum_{i=1}^{n}y_i\right)}{\sqrt{n\sum_{i=1}^{n}x_i^2 - \left(\sum_{i=1}^{n}x_i\right)^2}\sqrt{n\sum_{i=1}^{n}y_i^2 - \left(\sum_{i=1}^{n}y_i\right)^2}}$

$= \dfrac{12(480,565) - (4936)(1175)}{\sqrt{12(3,071,116) - (4936)^2}\sqrt{12(123,349) - (1175)^2}} = -0.030.$ The data do not suggest that

altitude affects home run hitting.

11.4.17 $r = \dfrac{17(4,759,470) - (7,973)(8,517)}{\sqrt{17(4,611,291) - (7,973)^2}\sqrt{17(5,421,917) - (8,517)^2}} = 0.762.$ The amount of variation

attributed to the linear regression is $r^2 = (0.762)^2 = 0.581$, or 58.1%.

Section 11.5

11.5.1 Y is a normal random variable with $E(Y) = 6$ and $\text{Var}(Y) = 10$. Then $P(5 < Y < 6.5) =$

$$P\left(\frac{5-6}{\sqrt{10}} < Z < \frac{6.5-6}{\sqrt{10}}\right) = P(-0.32 < Z < 0.16) = 0.5636 - 0.3745 = 0.1891. \text{ By Theorem}$$

11.5.1, $Y|2$ is normal with $E(Y|2) = \mu_Y + \dfrac{\rho\sigma_Y}{\sigma_X}(2 - \mu_X) = 6 + \dfrac{\frac{1}{2}\sqrt{10}}{2}(2-3) = 5.209$

$\text{Var}(Y|2) = (1-\rho^2)\sigma_Y^2 = (1 - 0.25)10 = 7.5$, so the standard deviation of Y is $\sqrt{7.5} = 2.739$.

$$P(5 < Y|2 < 6.5) = P\left(\frac{5 - 5.209}{2.739} < Z < \frac{6.5 - 5.209}{2.739}\right) = P(-0.08 < Z < 0.47) = 0.6808 - 0.4681$$

$= 0.2127$

11.5.3 **a)** $f_{X+Y}(t) = \dfrac{1}{2\pi\sqrt{1-\rho^2}} \displaystyle\int_{-\infty}^{\infty} \exp\left\{-\frac{1}{2}\left(\frac{1}{1-\rho^2}\right)\left[(t-y)^2 - 2\rho(t-y)y + y^2\right]\right\}dy$

The expression in the brackets can be expanded and rewritten as
$t^2 + 2(1+\rho)y^2 - 2t(1+\rho)y$
$= t^2 + 2(1+\rho)[y^2 - ty]$

$= t^2 + 2(1+\rho)\left[y^2 - ty + \dfrac{t^2}{4}\right] - \dfrac{1}{2}(1+\rho)t^2$

$= \dfrac{1-\rho}{2}t^2 + 2(1+\rho)(y - t/2)^2$. Placing this expression into the exponent gives

$$f_{X+Y}(t) = \frac{1}{2\pi\sqrt{1-\rho^2}}\, e^{-\frac{1}{2}\left(\frac{1}{1-\rho^2}\right)\frac{1-\rho}{2}t^2} \int_{-\infty}^{\infty} e^{-\frac{1}{2}\left(\frac{1}{1-\rho^2}\right)2(1+\rho)(y-t/2)^2}\,dy$$

$$= f_{X+Y}(t) = \frac{1}{2\pi\sqrt{1-\rho^2}}\, e^{-\frac{1}{2}\left(\frac{t^2}{2(1+\rho)}\right)} \int_{-\infty}^{\infty} e^{-\frac{1}{2}\left(\frac{(y-t/2)^2}{(1+\rho)/2}\right)}\,dy.$$

The integral is that of a normal pdf with mean $t/2$ and $\sigma^2 = (1+\rho)/2$.
Thus, the integral equals $\sqrt{2\pi(1+\rho)/2} = \sqrt{\pi(1+\rho)}$.
Putting this into the expression for f_{X+Y} gives

$$f_{X+Y}(t) = \frac{1}{\sqrt{2\pi}\sqrt{2(1+\rho)}}\, e^{-\frac{1}{2}\left(\frac{t^2}{2(1+\rho)}\right)}, \text{ which is the pdf of a normal variable with}$$

$\mu = 0$ and $\sigma^2 = 2(1+\rho)$.

b) $c\mu_X + d\mu_Y;\ c\sigma_X^2 + d\sigma_Y^2 + 2cd\sigma_X\sigma_Y\rho(X,Y)$

11.5.5 $E(X) = E(Y) = 0;\ \text{Var}(X) = 4;\ \text{Var}(Y) = 1;\ \rho(X, Y) = 1/2;\ k = 1/(2\pi\sqrt{3})$

11.5.7 $r = -0.453$. $T_{18} = \dfrac{\sqrt{n-2}\,r}{\sqrt{1-r^2}} = \dfrac{\sqrt{18}(-0.453)}{\sqrt{1-(-0.453)^2}} = -2.16$

Since $-t_{0.005,18} = -2.8784 < T_{18} = -2.16 < 2.8784 = t_{0.005,18}$, accept H_0.

11.5.9 From Question 11.4.15, $r = -0.030$. $T_{10} = \dfrac{\sqrt{10}(-0.030)}{\sqrt{1-(-0.030)^2}} = -0.09$.

Since $-t_{0.025,10} = -2.2281 < T_{10} = -0.09 < 2.2281 = t_{0.025,10}$, accept H_0.

11.5.11 From the Comment on page 626, we can deduce that

$$P\left(-z_{\alpha/2} < \frac{\frac{1}{2}\ln\frac{1+R}{1-R} - \frac{1}{2}\ln\frac{1+\rho}{1-\rho}}{\sqrt{\frac{1}{n-3}}} < z_{\alpha/2}\right) = 1 - \alpha$$

To find the confidence interval, we solve the inequality for ρ:

$$-z_{\alpha/2} < \frac{\frac{1}{2}\ln\frac{1+R}{1-R} - \frac{1}{2}\ln\frac{1+\rho}{1-\rho}}{\sqrt{\frac{1}{n-3}}} < z_{\alpha/2} \quad \text{implies}$$

$$-z_{\alpha/2}\sqrt{\frac{1}{n-3}} < \frac{1}{2}\ln\frac{1+R}{1-R} - \frac{1}{2}\ln\frac{1+\rho}{1-\rho} < z_{\alpha/2}\sqrt{\frac{1}{n-3}} \quad \text{or}$$

$$e^{-z_{\alpha/2}\sqrt{\frac{1}{n-3}}} < \sqrt{\frac{1+R}{1-R}} \Big/ \sqrt{\frac{1+\rho}{1-\rho}} < e^{z_{\alpha/2}\sqrt{\frac{1}{n-3}}}. \quad \text{Then}$$

$$\sqrt{\frac{1-R}{1+R}}\,e^{-z_{\alpha/2}\sqrt{\frac{1}{n-3}}} < \sqrt{\frac{1-\rho}{1+\rho}} < \sqrt{\frac{1-R}{1+R}}\,e^{z_{\alpha/2}\sqrt{\frac{1}{n-3}}}. \quad \text{Squaring the inequality gives}$$

$$\frac{1-R}{1+R}\,e^{-2z_{\alpha/2}\sqrt{\frac{1}{n-3}}} < \frac{1-\rho}{1+\rho} < \frac{1-R}{1+R}\,e^{2z_{\alpha/2}\sqrt{\frac{1}{n-3}}},$$

or $\dfrac{1-R}{1+R}\,e^{-2z_{\alpha/2}\sqrt{\frac{1}{n-3}}} < -1 + \dfrac{2}{1+\rho} < \dfrac{1-R}{1+R}\,e^{2z_{\alpha/2}\sqrt{\frac{1}{n-3}}}$. Solving this inequality for ρ yields the confidence interval:

$$1 + \frac{1-R}{1+R}\,e^{-2z_{\alpha/2}\sqrt{\frac{1}{n-3}}} < \frac{2}{1+\rho} < 1 + \frac{1-R}{1+R}\,e^{2z_{\alpha/2}\sqrt{\frac{1}{n-3}}}, \text{ which implies}$$

$$\frac{2}{1 + \frac{1-R}{1+R}\,e^{2z_{\alpha/2}\sqrt{\frac{1}{n-3}}}} < 1+\rho < \frac{2}{1 + \frac{1-R}{1+R}\,e^{-2z_{\alpha/2}\sqrt{\frac{1}{n-3}}}}, \text{ and finally}$$

$$-1 + \frac{2}{1 + \frac{1-R}{1+R}\,e^{2z_{\alpha/2}\sqrt{\frac{1}{n-3}}}} < \rho < -1 + \frac{2}{1 + \frac{1-R}{1+R}\,e^{-2z_{\alpha/2}\sqrt{\frac{1}{n-3}}}}$$

Chapter 12

Section 12.2

12.2.1 Here $n = 10$ and $k = 4$. To test H_0: $\mu_A = \mu_B = \mu_C = \mu_D$ at the $\alpha = 0.05$ level, reject the null hypothesis if $F \geq F_{.95,4-1,10-4} = 4.76$. At the $\alpha = 0.10$ level, H_0 is rejected if $F \geq F_{.90,3,6} = 3.29$. As the ANOVA table shows, the observed F falls between the two cutoffs, meaning that H_0 is rejected at the $\alpha = 0.10$ level, but not at the $\alpha = 0.05$ level.

Source	df	SS	MS	F
Model	3	61.33	20.44	3.94
Error	6	31.17	5.19	
Total	9	92.50		

12.2.3 For these $n = 30$ observations and $k = 3$ treatment groups, $C = T_{..}^2/n = (422.9)^2/30 = 5961.48$,

$$\text{SSTOT} = \sum_{j=1}^{3}\sum_{i=1}^{10} y_{ij}^2 - C = 914.1, \text{ and SSTR} = (121.4)^2/10 + (176.1)^2/10 + (125.4)^2/10 -$$

$5961.48 = 186.0$. To test the null hypothesis that the three types of stocks have equal price-earnings ratios, reject H_0 if $F \geq F_{.99,3-1,30-3} = F_{.99,2,27}$. The latter is not a cutoff that appears in Table A.4 of the Appendix. However, its value can be bounded by cutoffs with similar degrees of freedom that <u>are</u> listed: $F_{.99,2,30} = 5.39 < F_{.99,2,27} < F_{.99,2,24} = 5.61$. According to the ANOVA table, the observed F ratio equals 3.45, which implies that H_0 should not be rejected.

Source	df	SS	MS	F
Sector	2	186.0	93.0	3.45
Error	27	728.2	27.0	
Total	29	914.1		

12.2.5 To test at the $\alpha = 0.01$ level of significance the null hypothesis that the four tribes were contemporaries of one another, H_0 should be rejected if $F \geq F_{.99,4-1,12-4} = 7.59$ (or if $P < 0.01$). According to the ANOVA table, F is less than 7.59 (and P is greater than 0.01), so H_0 should not be rejected.

Source	df	SS	MS	F	P
Tribe	3	504167	168056	3.70	0.062
Error	8	363333	45417		
Total	11	867500			

12.2.7 The sample variances for Treatments A, C, and D are much smaller than the sample variance for Treatment D, suggesting that the assumption that σ^2 is the same for all treatment levels may not be true.

12.2.9 $\text{SSTE}/\sigma^2 = (1/\sigma^2)\sum_{j=1}^{k} n_j(\bar{Y}_{.j} - \bar{Y}_{..})^2 = (1/\sigma^2)\sum_{j=1}^{k} n_j[(\bar{Y}_{.j} - \mu) - (\bar{Y}_{..} - \mu)]^2 =$

$$(1/\sigma^2)\left[\sum_{j=1}^{k} n_j[(\bar{Y}_{.j} - \mu)^2 - n(\bar{Y}_{..} - \mu)^2\right] = \sum_{j=1}^{k}\left(\frac{\bar{Y}_{.j} - \mu}{\sigma/\sqrt{n_j}}\right)^2 - \left(\frac{\bar{Y}_{..} - \mu}{\sigma/\sqrt{n}}\right)^2.$$

Since the $\left(\dfrac{\bar{Y}_{.j} - \mu}{\sigma/\sqrt{n_j}}\right)$'s are independent normal random variables, and since $\left(\dfrac{\bar{Y}_{..} - \mu}{\sigma/\sqrt{n}}\right)$ can be

written as a linear combination of the $\left(\dfrac{\bar{Y}_{.j} - \mu}{\sigma/\sqrt{n_j}}\right)$'s, it follows from Fisher's lemma that

SSTR/σ^2 has a χ^2 distribution with $k - 1$ df.

12.2.11

Source	df	SS	MS	F	P
Author	1	0.002185	0.002185	15.04	0.001
Error	16	0.002325	0.000145		
Total	17	0.004510			

From Case Study 9.2.1, $t = 3.88$; except for a small rounding error, the square of the observed t ratio is the same as the observed F ratio: $(3.88)^2 = 15.05 \doteq 15.04$.

Section 12.3

12.3.1 For the data in Case Study 12.2.1, $k = 4$, $r = 6$, MSE $= 79.74$, and $D = Q_{.05,4,20}/\sqrt{6} =$ $3.96/\sqrt{6} = 1.617$. Let μ_1, μ_2, μ_3, and μ_4 denote the true average heart rates for Non-smokers, Light smokers, Moderate smokers, and Heavy smokers, respectively. Substituting into Theorem 12.3.1 gives the six different Tukey intervals summarized in the table below.

Pairwise Difference	Tukey interval	Conclusion
$\mu_1 - \mu_2$	(−15.27, 13.60)	NS
$\mu_1 - \mu_3$	(−23.77, 5.10)	NS
$\mu_1 - \mu_4$	(−33.77, −4.90)	Reject
$\mu_2 - \mu_3$	(−22.94, 5.94)	NS
$\mu_2 - \mu_4$	(−32.94, −4.06)	Reject
$\mu_3 - \mu_4$	(−24.44, 4.44)	NS

12.3.3 Let μ_C, μ_A, and μ_M denote the true average numbers of contaminant particles in IV fluids produced by Cutter, Abbott, and McGaw, respectively. According to the analysis of variance, H_0: $\mu_C = \mu_A = \mu_M$ is rejected at the $\alpha = 0.05$ level (since the P value is less than

Source	df	SS	MS	F	P
Company	2	113646	56823	5.81	0.014
Error	15	146754	9784		
Total	17	260400			

0.05). The three 95% Tukey confidence intervals (based on $k = 3$, $r = 6$, and $D = Q_{.05,3,15}/\sqrt{6} = 3.67/\sqrt{6} = 1.498$) show that Abbott and McGaw have the only pairwise difference $(204.50 - 396.67 = -192.17)$ that is statistically significant.

Pairwise Difference	Tukey interval	Conclusion
$\mu_C - \mu_A$	(−78.9, 217.5)	NS
$\mu_C - \mu_M$	(−271.0, 25.4)	NS
$\mu_A - \mu_M$	(−340.0, −44.0)	Reject

12.3.5 No. Look at the Tukey intervals constructed in Question 12.3.4, for example. The hypotheses H_0: $\mu_1 = \mu_3$ and H_0: $\mu_3 = \mu_4$ are rejected, but H_0: $\mu_1 = \mu_4$ is not.

Section 12.4

12.4.1

Source	df	SS	MS	F
Tube	2	510.7	255.4	11.56
Error	42	927.7	22.1	
Total	44	1438.4		

Subhypothesis	Contrast	SS	F
H_0: $\mu_A = \mu_C$	$C_1 = \mu_A - \mu_C$	264	11.95
H_0: $\mu_B = \dfrac{\mu_A + \mu_C}{2}$	$C_2 = \dfrac{1}{2}\mu_A - \mu_B + \dfrac{1}{2}\mu_C$	246.7	11.16

H_0: $\mu_A = \mu_B = \mu_C$ is strongly rejected ($F_{.99,2,42} \doteq F_{.99,2,40} = 5.18$). Theorem 12.4.1 holds true for orthogonal contrasts C_1 and C_2—$SS_{C_1} + SS_{C_2} = 264 + 246.7 = 510.7 = SSTR$. Also, both subhypotheses would be rejected—their F ratios exceed $F_{.99,1,42}$.

12.4.3 Let μ_1, μ_2, μ_3, and μ_4 denote the true average heart rates for Non-smokers, Light smokers, Moderate smokers, and Heavy smokers, respectively. To test H_0: $(\mu_2 + \mu_3)/2 = \mu_4$, let $C = \dfrac{1}{2}\mu_2 + \dfrac{1}{2}\mu_3 - \mu_4$, so $\hat{C} = \dfrac{1}{2}(63.2) + \dfrac{1}{2}(71.7) - 1(81.7) = -14.25$. Also, $SS_C = (-14.25)^2 / \left[\dfrac{(1/2)^2}{6} + \dfrac{(1/2)^2}{6} + \dfrac{(-1)^2}{6}\right] = 812.25$. From the ANOVA table on p. 642, $SSE = 1594.833$ and $n - k = 20$. Therefore, H_0 should be rejected if $F \geq F_{.95,1,20} = 4.35$. Here $F = \dfrac{812.25/1}{1594.833/20} = 10.19$, so H_0: $(\mu_2 + \mu_3)/2 = \mu_4$ is rejected (at the $\alpha = 0.05$ level).

12.4.5

	μ_A	μ_B	μ_C	μ_D	$\sum_{j=1}^{4} c_j$
C_1	1	-1	0	0	0
C_2	0	0	1	-1	0
C_3	$\dfrac{11}{12}$	$\dfrac{11}{12}$	-1	$\dfrac{-5}{6}$	0

C_1 and C_3 are orthogonal because $\dfrac{1(11/12)}{6} + \dfrac{(-1)(11/12)}{6} = 0$; also, C_2 and C_3 are orthogonal because $\dfrac{1(-1)}{6} + \dfrac{(-1)(-5/6)}{5} = 0$. $\hat{C}_3 = -2.293$ and $SS_{C_3} = 8.97$. But $SS_{C_1} + SS_{C_2} + SS_{C_3} = 4.68 + 1.12 + 8.97 = 14.77 = SSTR$.

Section 12.5

12.5.1 Replace each observation by its square root. At the $\alpha = 0.05$ level, H_0: $\mu_A = \mu_B$ is rejected. (For $\alpha = 0.01$, though, we would fail to reject H_0).

Source	df	SS	MS	F	P
Developer	1	1.836	1.836	6.23	0.032
Error	10	2.947	0.295		
Total	11	4.783			

12.5.3 Since Y_{ij} is a binomial random variable based on $n = 20$ trials, each data point should be replaced by the arcsin of $(y_{ij}/20)^{\frac{1}{2}}$. Based on those transformed observations, H_0: $\mu_A = \mu_B = \mu_C$ is strongly rejected ($P < 0.001$).

Source	df	SS	MS	F	P
Launcher	2	0.30592	0.15296	22.34	0.000
Error	9	0.06163	0.00685		
Total	11	0.36755			

Appendix 12.A.3

12.A.3.1 The F test will have greater power against H_1^{**} because the latter yields a larger noncentrality parameter than does H_1^*.

12.A.3.3 $M_V(t) = (1-2t)^{-r/2} e^{\gamma t(1-2t)^{-1}}$, so $M_V^{(1)}(t) = (1-2t)^{-r/2} \cdot e^{\gamma t(1-2t)^{-1}} [\gamma t(-1)(1-2t)^{-2}(-2) + (1-2t)^{-1}\gamma] + e^{\gamma t(1-2t)^{-1}} \left(-\dfrac{r}{2}\right)(1-2t)^{-(r/2)-1}(-2)$. Therefore, $E(V) = M_V^{(1)}(0) = \gamma + r$.

12.A.3.5 $M_V(t) = \prod_{i=1}^{n}(1-2t)^{-r_i/2}e^{\gamma_i t/(1-2t)} = (1-2t)^{-\sum_{i=1}^{n}r_i/2} \cdot e^{\left(\sum_{i=1}^{n}\gamma_i\right)t/(1-2t)}$, which implies that V has a

noncentral χ^2 distribution with $\sum_{i=1}^{n}r_i$ df and with noncentrality parameter $\sum_{i=1}^{n}\gamma_i$.

Chapter 13

Section 13.2

13.2.1

Source	df	SS	MS	F	P
States	1	61.63	61.63	7.20	0.0178
Students	14	400.80	28.63	3.34	0.0155
Error	14	119.87	8.56		
Total	29	582.30			

The critical value $F_{0.95,1,14}$ is approximately 4.6. Since the F statistic $= 7.20 > 4.6$, reject H_0.

13.2.3

Source	df	SS	MS	F	P
Additive	1	0.03	0.03	4.19	0.0865
Batch	6	0.02	0.00	0.41	0.8483
Error	6	0.05	0.01		
Total	13	0.10			

Since the F statistic $= 4.19 < F_{0.95,1,6} = 5.99$, accept H_0.

13.2.5

Source	df	SS	MS	F	P
Quarter	3	0.60	0.20	0.60	0.6272
Year	4	19.87	4.97	14.85	0.0001
Error	12	4.01	0.33		
Total	19	24.48			

Since the F statistic for treatments $= 0.60 < F_{0.95,3,12} = 3.49$, accept H_0 that yields are not affected by the quarter.
Since the F statistic for blocks $= 14.85 > F_{0.95,4,12} = 3.26$, reject H_0; yields do depend on the year.

13.2.7 From Question 13.2.2 we obtain the value MSE $= 0.98$. The radius of the interval is
$$D\sqrt{MSE} = (Q_{0.05,3,6}/\sqrt{b})\sqrt{0.98} = (4.34/\sqrt{4})\sqrt{0.98} = 2.148.$$

The Tukey intervals are

Pairwise Difference	$\bar{y}_{.s} - \bar{y}_{.t}$	Tukey Interval	Conclusion
$\mu_1 - \mu_2$	2.925	(0.78, 5.07)	Reject
$\mu_1 - \mu_3$	1.475	(−0.67, 3.62)	NS
$\mu_2 - \mu_3$	−1.450	(−3.60, 0.70)	NS

13.2.9 a)

Source	df	SS	MS	F	P
Sleep phases	2	16.99	8.49	4.13	0.0493
Shrew	5	195.44	39.09	19.00	0.0001
Error	10	20.57	2.06		
Total	17	233.00			

Since the F statistic $= 4.13 > F_{0.95, 2, 10} = 4.10$, reject H_0.

b)   The contrast associated with the subhypothesis is

$$C_1 = -\frac{1}{2}\mu_1 - \frac{1}{2}\mu_2 + \mu_3, \text{ and } \hat{C}_1 = -\frac{1}{2}(21.1) - \frac{1}{2}(19.1) + 18.983 = -1.117$$

$$SS_{C_1} = \frac{(-1.117)^2}{\left(-\frac{1}{2}\right)^2/6 + \left(-\frac{1}{2}\right)^2/6 + (1)^2/6} = 4.99.$$

$$F = \frac{SS_{C_1}}{MSE} = \frac{4.99}{2.06} = 2.42. \text{ Since the observed } F \text{ ratio} = 2.42 < F_{0.95, 1, 10} = 4.96,$$
accept the subhypothesis.

Let a second orthogonal contrast be $C_2 = \mu_1 - \mu_2$.

$$\hat{C}_2 = 21.1 - 19.1 = 2.0. \quad SS_{C_2} = \frac{2.0^2}{(1)^2/6 + (-1)^2/6} = 12.0$$

Then $SSTR = 16.99 = 4.99 + 12.00 = SS_{C_1} + SS_{C_2}$

13.2.11 Equation 13.2.2:

$$SSTR = \sum_{i=1}^{b}\sum_{j=1}^{k}(\bar{Y}_{.j} - \bar{Y}_{..})^2 = b\sum_{j=1}^{k}(\bar{Y}_{.j} - \bar{Y}..)^2$$

$$= b\sum_{j=1}^{k}(\bar{Y}_{.j}^2 - 2\bar{Y}_{.j}\bar{Y}_{..} + \bar{Y}_{..}^2) = b\sum_{j=1}^{k}\bar{Y}_{.j}^2 - 2b\bar{Y}_{..}\sum_{j=1}^{k}\bar{Y}_{.j} + bk\bar{Y}_{..}^2$$

$$= b\sum_{j=1}^{k}\frac{T_{.j}^2}{b^2} - \frac{2T_{..}^2}{bk} + \frac{T_{..}^2}{bk} = \sum_{j=1}^{k}\frac{T_{.j}^2}{b} - \frac{T_{..}^2}{bk} = \sum_{j=1}^{k}\frac{T_{.j}^2}{b} - c$$

Equation 13.2.3:

$$SSB = \sum_{i=1}^{b}\sum_{j=1}^{k}(\bar{Y}_{i.} - \bar{Y}_{..})^2 = k\sum_{i=1}^{b}(\bar{Y}_{i.} - \bar{Y}_{..})^2$$

$$= k\sum_{i=1}^{b}(\bar{Y}_{i.}^2 - 2\bar{Y}_{i.}\bar{Y}_{..} + \bar{Y}_{..}^2) = k\sum_{i=1}^{b}\bar{Y}_{i.}^2 - 2k\bar{Y}_{..}\sum_{i=1}^{b}\bar{Y}_{i.} + bk\bar{Y}_{..}^2$$

$$= k\sum_{i=1}^{b}\frac{T_{i.}^2}{k^2} - \frac{2T_{..}^2}{bk} + \frac{T_{..}^2}{bk} = \sum_{i=1}^{b}\frac{T_{i.}^2}{k} - \frac{T_{..}^2}{bk} = \sum_{i=1}^{b}\frac{T_{i.}^2}{k} - c$$

Equation 13.2.4:

$$\text{SSTOT} = \sum_{i=1}^{b}\sum_{j=1}^{k}(Y_{ij} - \bar{Y}_{..})^2 = \sum_{i=1}^{b}\sum_{j=1}^{k}(Y_{ij}^2 - 2Y_{ij}\bar{Y}_{..} + \bar{Y}_{..}^2)$$

$$\sum_{i=1}^{b}\sum_{j=1}^{k}Y_{ij}^2 - 2\bar{Y}_{..}\sum_{i=1}^{b}\sum_{j=1}^{k}Y_{ij} + bk\bar{Y}_{..}^2$$

$$= \sum_{i=1}^{b}\sum_{j=1}^{k}Y_{ij}^2 - \frac{2T_{..}^2}{bk} + \frac{T_{..}^2}{bk} = \sum_{i=1}^{b}\sum_{j=1}^{k}Y_{ij}^2 - c$$

13.2.13 a)   False. $\displaystyle\sum_{i=1}^{b}\bar{Y}_{i.} = \frac{1}{k}\sum_{i=1}^{b}\sum_{j=1}^{k}Y_{ij}$. $\displaystyle\sum_{j=1}^{k}\bar{Y}_{.j} = \frac{1}{b}\sum_{i=1}^{b}\sum_{j=1}^{k}Y_{ij}$. The two expressions are equal only when $b = k$.

b)   False. If neither treatment levels nor blocks are significant, it is possible to have F variables $\dfrac{\text{SSTR}/(k-1)}{\text{SSE}/(b-1)(k-1)}$ and $\dfrac{\text{SSB}/(b-1)}{\text{SSE}/(b-1)(k-1)}$ both < 1.
In that case both SSTR and SSB are less than SSE.

Section 13.3

13.3.1 Test H_0: $\mu_D = 0$ vs H_1: $\mu_D > 0$.

$$s_D^2 = \frac{b\displaystyle\sum_{i=1}^{b}d_i^2 - \left(\displaystyle\sum_{i=1}^{b}d_i\right)^2}{b(b-1)} = \frac{12(11.7229)-(8.55)^2}{12(11)} = 0.512$$

$$t = \frac{\bar{d}}{s_D/\sqrt{b}} = \frac{0.7125}{\sqrt{0.512}/\sqrt{12}} = 3.45$$

Since $3.45 > 1.3634 = t_{0.10,11}$, reject H_0.

13.3.3 Test H_0: $\mu_D = 0$ vs. H_1: $\mu_D \neq 0$.

$$s_D^2 = \frac{b\displaystyle\sum_{i=1}^{b}d_i^2 - \left(\displaystyle\sum_{i=1}^{b}d_i\right)^2}{b(b-1)} = \frac{12(2.97)-(1.3)^2}{12(11)} = 0.257$$

$$t = \frac{\bar{d}}{s_D/\sqrt{b}} = \frac{1.108}{\sqrt{0.257}/\sqrt{12}} = 0.74.$$

$\alpha = 0.05$: Since $-t_{0.025,11} = -2.2010 < 0.74 < 2.2010 = t_{0.025,11}$, accept H_0.
$\alpha = 0.01$: Since $-t_{0.005,11} = -3.1058 < 0.74 < 3.1058 = t_{0.005,11}$ accept H_0.

13.3.5 Test H_0: $\mu_D = 0$ vs. H_1: $\mu_D \neq 0$.

$$s_D^2 = \frac{7(0.1653) - (-0.69)^2}{7(6)} = 0.01621$$

$$t = \frac{-0.09857}{\sqrt{0.01621/\sqrt{7}}} = -2.048.$$

Since $-t_{0.025,6} = -2.4469 < -2.048 < 2.4469 = t_{0.025,6}$ accept H_0.
The square of the observed Student t statistic $= (-2.048)^2 = 4.194 =$ the observed F statistic.
Also, $(t_{0.025,6})^2 = (2.4469)^2 = 5.987 = F_{0.95,1,6}$
Conclusion: the two-sided test for paired data is equivalent to the randomized block design test for 2 treatments.

13.3.7 The 95% confidence interval is $\left(\bar{d} - t_{0.025,11} \dfrac{s_D}{\sqrt{b}}, \ \bar{d} + t_{0.025,11} \dfrac{s_D}{\sqrt{b}} \right)$

$$= \left(0.108 - 2.2010 \frac{\sqrt{0.257}}{\sqrt{12}}, \ 0.108 + 2.2010 \frac{\sqrt{0.257}}{\sqrt{12}} \right) = (-0.21, 0.43)$$

Chapter 14

Section 14.2

14.2.1 Let $p = P(Y_i > X_i)$. For $\alpha = 0.05$, we should reject H_0: $p = 1/2$ in favor or H_1: $p < 1/2$, if $y_+ \leq$ 2. This choice of critical value is because $P(Y_+ \leq 2) =$

$$\left[\binom{11}{0} + \binom{11}{1} + \binom{11}{2}\right]\left(\frac{1}{2}\right)^{11} = 0.033, \text{ and } P(Y_+ = 3)\ \binom{11}{3}\left(\frac{1}{2}\right)^{11} = 0.081.$$

x_i	y_i	$y_i > x_i$?
15	13	−
12	8	−
12	12.5	+
14	12	−
13	12	−
13	12.5	−
13	12.5	−
12	14	+
12.5	12	−
12	11	−
12.5	10	−

From the table, $y_+ = 2$. Thus, reject H_0.

14.2.3 Let Y_+ denote the number of Y_i for which $Y_i - 7.39 > 0$. Omit the observation where $Y_i = 7.39$. For the 43 remaining observations, $y_+ = 4$. Here n is large enough to use the DeMoivre-Laplace approximation.

Take $z = \dfrac{y_+ - \frac{1}{2}n}{\sqrt{n/4}} = \dfrac{4 - \frac{1}{2}(43)}{\sqrt{43/4}} = -5.34$. Since the observed Z ratio $= -5.34 < -2.58 = -z_{0.005}$, reject H_0.

14.2.5 $P(Y_+ = y_+) = \binom{7}{y_+}\dfrac{1}{2^7}$. These values are given in the table.

y_+	$P(Y_+ = y_+)$
0	1/128
1	7/128
2	21/128
3	35/128
4	35/128
5	21/128
6	7/128
7	1/128

Possible levels for a one-sided test: 1/128, 8/128, 29/128, etc.

14.2.7

y_i	$y_i - 0.80$	sign	y_i	$y_i - 0.80$	sign
0.61	−0.19	−	0.78	−0.02	−
0.70	−0.10	−	0.84	0.04	+
0.63	−0.17	−	0.83	0.03	+
0.76	−0.04	−	0.82	0.02	+
0.67	−0.13	−	0.74	−0.06	−
0.72	−0.08	−	0.85	0.05	+
0.64	−0.16	−	0.73	−0.07	−
0.82	0.02	+	0.85	0.05	+
0.88	0.08	+	0.87	0.07	+
0.82	0.02	+			

$$\sum_{k=0}^{6}\binom{19}{k}\left(\frac{1}{2}\right)^{19} = 0.0835, \text{ while } \sum_{k=0}^{7}\binom{19}{k}\left(\frac{1}{2}\right)^{19} = 0.1796. \text{ Thus, the closest test to one with } \alpha =$$

0.10 is to reject H_0 if $y_+ \leq 6$. This test has $\alpha = 0.0835$. Since $y_+ = 9$, accept H_0. Since the observed t statistic $= -1.71 < -1.330 = -t_{0.10,18}$, the t test rejects H_0.

14.2.9 $z = \dfrac{y_+ - \dfrac{1}{2}n}{\sqrt{n/4}} = \dfrac{19 - \dfrac{1}{2}(28)}{\sqrt{28/4}} = 1.89$. Accept H_0, since $-z_{0.025} = -1.96 < 1.89 < 1.96 = z_{0.025}$.

Section 14.3

14.3.1

x_i	y_i	$y_i - x_i$	$|y_i - x_i|$	r_i	z_i	$r_i z_i$
1458	1424	−34	34	1	0	0
1353	1501	148	148	5	1	5
2209	1495	−714	714	8	0	0
1804	1739	−65	65	2	0	0
1912	2031	119	119	4	1	4
1366	934	−432	432	7	0	0
1598	1401	−197	197	6	0	0
1406	1339	−67	67	3	0	0

The sum of the $r_i z_i$ column is 9. From Table A.6, the critical values of 7 and 29 give $\alpha = 0.148$. Since $7 < w = 9 < 29$, accept H_0.

14.3.3

x_i	y_i	$y_i - x_i$	$\lvert y_i - x_i \rvert$	r_i	z_i	$r_i z_i$
16.5	16.9	0.4	0.4	12.5	1	12.5
17.6	17.2	−0.4	0.4	12.5	0	0
16.9	17.0	0.1	0.1	2	1	2
15.8	16.1	0.3	0.3	8.5	1	8.5
18.4	18.2	−0.2	0.2	4.5	0	0
17.5	17.7	0.2	0.2	4.5	1	4.5
17.6	17.9	0.3	0.3	8.5	1	8.5
16.1	16.0	−0.1	0.1	2	0	0
16.8	17.3	0.5	0.5	14	1	14
15.8	16.1	0.3	0.3	8.5	1	8.5
16.8	16.5	−0.3	0.3	8.5	0	0
17.3	17.6	0.3	0.3	8.5	1	8.5
18.1	18.4	0.3	0.3	8.5	1	8.5
17.9	17.2	−0.7	0.7	15	0	0
16.4	16.5	0.1	0.1	2	1	2

w = sum of the $r_i z_i$ column is 77.5. The mean of W is $n(n + 1)/4 = 60$. The variance of $W =$ $n(n + 1)(2n + 1)/24 = 310$. The observed Z statistic $w' = \dfrac{77.5 - 60}{\sqrt{310}} = 0.99$.

Since $-1.96 < w' = 0.99 < 1.96 = z_{0.025}$, accept H_0.

14.3.5

y_i	$y_i - 0.80$	$\lvert y_i - 0.80 \rvert$	r_i	z_i	$r_i z_i$
0.61	−0.19	0.19	19	0	0
0.70	−0.10	0.10	15	0	0
0.63	−0.17	0.17	18	0	0
0.76	−0.04	0.04	6.5	0	0
0.67	−0.13	0.13	16	0	0
0.72	−0.08	0.08	13.5	0	0
0.64	−0.16	0.16	17	0	0
0.82	0.02	0.02	2.5	1	2.5
0.88	0.08	0.08	13.5	1	13.5
0.82	0.02	0.02	2.5	1	2.5
0.78	−0.02	0.02	2.5	0	0
0.84	0.04	0.04	6.5	1	6.5
0.83	0.03	0.03	5	1	5
0.82	0.02	0.02	2.5	1	2.5
0.74	−0.06	0.06	10	0	0
0.85	0.05	0.05	8.5	1	8.5
0.73	−0.07	0.07	11.5	0	0
0.85	0.05	0.05	8.5	1	8.5
0.87	0.07	0.07	11.5	1	11.5

w = sum of the $r_i z_i$ column = 61. The mean of W is $n(n + 1)/4 = 95$. The variance of $W = n(n + 1)(2n + 1)/24 = 617.5$. The observed Z statistic $w' = \dfrac{61 - 95}{\sqrt{617.5}} = -1.37$. Since $w' = -1.37 < -1.28 = -z_{0.10}$, reject H_0. The sign test accepted H_0.

14.3.7 The signed rank test should have more power since it uses a greater amount of the information in the data.

Section 14.4

14.4.1 Inadequate mixing of the capsules in the bowl.

14.4.3

Amer. Male	Rank	Eur. Male	Rank
5.9	7	6.2	8.5
6.8	12	5.3	2
6.4	10	5.6	4
7.0	14	5.5	3
6.6	11	5.1	1
7.7	16	6.2	8.5
7.2	15	5.8	5.5
6.9	13	5.8	5.5

Summing the second column in the table gives $r_{.1} = 98$, and the sum of the fourth column is $r_{.2} = 38$. The test statistic is $b = \dfrac{12}{n(n+1)}\left(\dfrac{r_{.1}^2}{n_1} + \dfrac{r_{.2}^2}{n_2}\right) - 3(n+1)$

$$= \dfrac{12}{16(17)}\left(\dfrac{98^2}{8} + \dfrac{38^2}{8}\right) - 3(17) = 9.93.$$

Since $b = 9.93 > 3.841 = \chi^2_{0.95,1}$, reject H_0.

14.4.5

Non-Smokers	Rank	Light Smokers	Rank	Moderate Smokers	Rank	Heavy Smokers	Rank
69	13	55	2	66	10.5	91	23
52	1	60	7	81	20.5	72	16
71	15	78	18	70	14	81	20.5
58	4.5	58	4.5	77	17	67	12
59	6	62	8	57	3	95	24
65	9	66	10.5	79	19	84	22

$$b = \dfrac{12}{n(n+1)}\left(\dfrac{r_{.1}^2}{n_1} + \dfrac{r_{.2}^2}{n_2} + \dfrac{r_{.3}^2}{n_3} + \dfrac{r_{.4}^2}{n_4}\right) - 3(n+1)$$

$$= \dfrac{12}{24(25)}\left(\dfrac{48.5^2}{6} + \dfrac{50^2}{6} + \dfrac{84^2}{6} + \dfrac{117.5^2}{6}\right) - 3(25) = 10.715$$

Since $b = 10.715 > 7.815 = \chi^2_{0.95,3}$, reject H_0.

14.4.7

Powered	Rank	Moderate	Rank	Coarse	Rank
146	8.5	150	14.5	141	4
152	16	144	6	138	2
149	12.5	148	10.5	142	5
161	21	155	19	146	8.5
158	20	154	17.5	139	3
149	12.5	150	14.5	145	7
154	17.5	148	10.5	137	1

$$b = \frac{12}{n(n+1)}\left(\frac{r_{.1}^2}{n_1} + \frac{r_{.2}^2}{n_2} + \frac{r_{.3}^2}{n_3}\right) - 3(n+1)$$

$$= \frac{12}{21(22)}\left(\frac{108^2}{7} + \frac{92.5^2}{7} + \frac{30.5^2}{7}\right) - 3(22) = 12.48$$

Since $b = 12.48 > 5.991 = \chi_{0.95,2}^2$, reject H_0.

Section 14.5

14.5.1

36 lb.	Rank	54 lb.	Rank	72 lb.	Rank	108 lb.	Rank	144 lb.	Rank
7.62	3	8.14	5	7.76	4	7.17	1	7.46	2
8.00	4	8.15	5	7.73	3	7.57	1	7.68	2
7.93	5	7.87	4	7.74	2	7.80	3	7.21	1

$$g = \frac{12}{bk(k+1)}\sum_{j=1}^{5} r_{.j}^2 - 3b(k+1)$$

$$= \frac{12}{3(5)(6)}(12^2 + 14^2 + 9^2 + 5^2 + 5^2) - 3(3)(6)$$

Since $g = 8.8 < 9.488 = \chi_{0.95,4}^2$, accept H_0.

14.5.3

PcrCh1	Rank	Davies	Rank	AOAC	Rank
0.598	1	0.628	2	0.632	3
0.614	1	0.628	2	0.630	3
0.600	1.5	0.600	1.5	0.622	3
0.580	1	0.612	3	0.584	2
0.596	1	0.600	2	0.650	3
0.592	1	0.628	3	0.606	2
0.616	1	0.628	2	0.644	3
0.614	1	0.644	2.5	0.644	2.5
0.604	1	0.644	3	0.624	2
0.608	1	0.612	2	0.619	3
0.602	1	0.628	2	0.632	3
0.614	1	0.644	3	0.616	2

$$g = \frac{12}{bk(k+1)} \sum_{j=1}^{3} r_{\cdot j}^2 - 3b(k+1)$$

$$= \frac{12}{12(3)(4)} (12.5^2 + 28^2 + 31.5^2) - 3(12)(4) = 17.0$$

Since $g = 17.0 > 5.991 = \chi_{0.95,2}^2$ reject H_0.

14.5.5 a)

Common Fund	Rank	3 Mo. Treasury	Rank
6.71	2	5.75	1
6.19	2	5.51	1
6.23	2	5.38	1
6.07	2	5.17	1
5.63	2	4.73	1
6.86	2	4.19	1
3.93	1.5	3.93	1.5
3.95	1.5	3.95	1.5
4.16	1.5	4.16	1.5
4.26	2	3.83	1
4.26	2	3.75	1
4.41	2	3.76	1

$$g = \frac{12}{bk(k+1)} \sum_{j=1}^{2} r_{\cdot j}^2 - 3b(k+1)$$

$$= \frac{12}{12(2)(3)} (22.5^2 + 13.5^2) - 3(12)(3) = 6.75$$

Since $g = 6.75 > 3.841 = \chi_{0.95,1}^2$ reject H_0.

b)

x_i	y_i	$y_i - x_i$	$|y_i - x_i|$	r_i	z_i	$r_i z_i$
6.71	5.75	−0.96	0.96	8	0	0
6.19	5.51	−0.68	0.68	4	0	0
6.23	5.38	−0.85	0.85	5	0	0
6.07	5.17	−0.90	0.90	6.5	0	0
5.63	4.73	−0.90	0.90	6.5	0	0
6.86	4.19	−2.67	2.67	9	0	0
4.26	3.83	−0.43	0.43	1	0	0
4.26	3.75	−0.51	0.51	2	0	0
4.41	3.76	−0.65	0.65	3	0	0

Dropping out those observations with $x_i = y_i$ gives $n = 9$. A hypothesis test of level = 0.054 rejects H_0 if $w \leq 6$ or $w \geq 39$. (see Table A.6). Since the observed Wilcoxon statistic is 0, reject H_0.